PUBLIC HEALTH

IMPROVING POLICY IN TURBULENT TIMES

UNDER SIEGE

For access to digital chapters and other eproducts, visit the APHA Press bookstore (www.apha.org).

PUBLIC HEALTH

IMPROVING POLICY IN TURBULENT TIMES

UNDER SIEGE

Brian C. Castrucci, DrPH
Georges Benjamin, MD
Grace Guerrero Ramirez, MSPH
Grace Castillo, MPH

American Public Health Association
800 I Street, NW
Washington, DC 20001-3710
www.apha.org

Georges C. Benjamin, MD, Executive Director

Printed and bound in the United States of America
Book Production Editor: Blair Reynolds
Typesetting: KnowledgeWorks Global Ltd.
Cover Design: Abduallahi Abdulgader
Printing and Binding: Sheridan Books

Library of Congress Cataloging-in-Publication Data

Names: Castrucci, Brian C., editor. | Benjamin, Georges, editor. | Guerrero
   Ramirez, Grace, editor. | Castillo, Grace, editor.
Title: Public health under siege : improving policy in turbulent times /
   edited by Brian C. Castrucci, DrPH, Georges Benjamin, MD, Grace Guerrero
   Ramirez, MSPH, Grace Castillo, MPH.
Description: Washington, DC : American Public Health Association, [2021] |
   Includes bibliographical references and index. | Summary: "For those who
   seek to improve health through policy change, this book is intended to
   be your companion. It is written by practitioners, elected officials,
   and other policymakers who have firsthand experience with the complex
   dynamics of policymaking through their professional careers. Its
   chapters share perspectives on the power of policy from the federal,
   state, and local levels; demonstrate several evidence-based policy
   packages developed by leading public health organizations; provide
   perspectives not only on legislative policy but on the roles of
   litigation and regulation; and reveal the existing threats to using
   policy to impact health. We hope that this book will inspire current and
   future public health practitioners and policymakers to use policy to
   achieve optimal and equitable health for all"-- Provided by publisher.
Identifiers: LCCN 2021007937 (print) | LCCN 2021007938 (ebook) | ISBN
   9780875533193 (paperback) | ISBN 9780875533209 (ebook)
Subjects: LCSH: Public health. | Medical policy.
Classification: LCC RA425 .P837 2021 (print) | LCC RA425 (ebook) | DDC
   362.1--dc23
LC record available at https://lccn.loc.gov/2021007937
LC ebook record available at https://lccn.loc.gov/2021007938

Contents

Acknowledgments   ix

1.   Why Policy Matters   1
     Brian C. Castrucci and Georges Benjamin

I. THE POWER OF POLICY AT THE FEDERAL, STATE,
   AND LOCAL LEVELS   5

2.   Federal Policy for Health   7
     Edward L. Hunter

3.   The Adverse Impact of Federal Health Policies
     on Health, Migration, and the Economy:
     The Case of Puerto Rico   13
     Maria Levis-Peralta and Grace Guerrero Ramirez

4.   The State Perspective   19
     John Auerbach and Monica Valdes Lupi

5.   From the Roots Up: The Critical Role
     of Local Action in Policy Change   25
     Colleen Bridger and Ron Nirenberg

II. EXISTING POLICY TOOLS AND FRAMEWORKS   31

6.   The CityHealth Framework   33
     Catherine Patterson and Grace Castillo

7.   Using the Health Impact in Five Years (HI-5) Model   39
     Elizabeth L. Skillen and Meghan Roney

8. Learning From the Promoting Health and Cost Control
in States (PHACCS) Initiative: How States Can Implement
Evidence-Based Policy to Address Health Inequities and
Improve Population Health   49
Adam Lustig

III. DIFFERENT TOOLS, SAME GOAL   55

9. Politics as a Public Health Imperative   57
Abdul El-Sayed

10. The Power of Regulatory Policy   61
Joshua M. Sharfstein

11. The Power of Litigation   67
Kendall Stagg, Derek Carr, and Todd Fraley

**IV. THREATS TO USING POLICY AS A TOOL FOR
PUBLIC HEALTH**   81

12. Perils of Preemption: When State Laws Conflict
With Local Policies   83
*Christiana K. McFarland, David H. Jernigan, and
Shelley Hearne*

13. How We Fight With Both Hands and Win   91
Jake Williams

V. ADVOCACY IN ACTION   99

14. You Don't Ask, You Don't Get: A Case Study in
Building Coalitions for Public Health Funding   101
Emily J. Holubowich

15. #SpeakForHealth   107
Susan L. Polan

16. Embracing Incrementalism   113
Patrick Guerriero

17.   Ensuring Policy Impact Through Strong Legal Practice   117
      Marice Ashe

**VI. CASE STUDIES IN COURAGE: POLICY APPROACHES TO
     THE SOCIAL DETERMINANTS OF HEALTH**   123

18.   Gun Safety in America: From Tragedy to Transformation   125
      Dannel P. Malloy

19.   Housing: A Case Study in Rental Inspection Policy in
      Kansas City, Missouri   131
      Rex Archer and Stacie Duitsman

20.   Early Education: Why Quality Pre-K Is Worth the Investment   135
      Ellen Frede and W. Steven Barnett

21.   Tobacco Control: Going Smoke-Free Deep in Tobacco Country   141
      Karen Remley

22.   Economic Security and Health:
      Making the Case for Paid Sick Leave   147
      Lili Farhang and Jonathan Heller

23.   Environmental Health: Critical Issues for Our Children   153
      Nsedu Witherspoon

24.   Moving Elimination of Racism From the Margins to
      the Center of Health Policy   159
      Gail C. Christopher

25.   Conclusion: Framing the Future of Public Health Policy   171
      Grace Guerrero Ramirez and Grace Castillo

Contributors   175

Index   179

Acknowledgments

We want to acknowledge all the contributors, colleagues, and reviewers that made this book possible. The authors' enthusiasm, effort, time, and responsiveness throughout this process has been invaluable—especially as we responded to and coped with the challenges and devastation of COVID-19.

We thank Abigail Johnson, Catherine Patterson, and Julia Haskins for their insights and unwavering assistance throughout the chapter ideation, drafting and review phases, as well as other colleagues at the de Beaumont Foundation. We want to acknowledge Pete de Beaumont, James Sprague, and the entire de Beaumont Foundation Board of Directors for creating an organization with the courage and willingness to pursue policy change to improve health.

Our gratitude extends to Blair Reynolds and the rest of the editorial and leadership team at the American Public Health Association for their thoughtfulness and diligence in crafting this book.

The editors are especially indebted to and inspired by the many courageous advocates leading the path towards a just and thriving society using policy as a tool.

Lead on,
Brian C. Castrucci, DrPH
Georges Benjamin, MD
Grace Guerrero Ramirez, MSPH
Grace Castillo, MPH

Why Policy Matters

Brian C. Castrucci, DrPH and Georges Benjamin, MD

William Shakespeare wrote, "All the world's a stage, And all the men and women merely players." Policy sets that stage. There are fancier definitions, but truly understanding this is critical to recognizing the outsized importance that policy has on our health. A frayed social safety net, economic and housing instability, racism and other forms of discrimination, educational disparities, inadequate nutrition, and risks within the physical environment all have indelible impacts on our health. Despite concerted efforts, we cannot manage or mediate these drivers of poor health through programs and interventions, prescriptions, or clinical engagements. Policy is the path toward changing these and other similar issues; toward changing the stage.

Policy has increased life expectancy and improved health. Occupational safety policies, for example, set new workplace practice and safety standards that have prevented tens of thousands of employee deaths each year in contrast to 1930s labor practices.[1] Policies that increased vehicle safety, required car safety seats for infants and children and seat belt use for adults, and increased penalties for drunk and impaired driving have lowered the number of deaths per mile traveled, while we have significantly increased the number of miles we drive.[2] Tobacco use has reached historic lows through a combination of limits on advertising, increases in taxes, and requirements for clean indoor air.[3] This is only a sampling of the policies that contributed to a 30-year increase in life expectancy between 1900 (47 years) and 1999 (77 years). Since the start of the 21st century,[4] the definition of health policy has broadened to include minimum wage increases, paid sick leave requirements, proactive rental inspection, and housing trusts, all of which can help reduce economic and health disparities. While we often focus our attention on creating and implementing new policies, it is equally important to redress those policies that perpetuate inequities. There are decades of racist and exclusionary state and federal policies that contribute to health inequities and poor outcomes that must be changed or removed.

Despite the critical importance of policy to health and equity, most Americans view access to health care as the major driver of our health. People remember going to the doctor—the feeling of being sick and then being restored to health. But people cannot recall the illnesses they never had because of clean drinking water and safer food. Access to health care is an important and visible determinant of health, but it is not the most influential. Yet the United States uses both fiscal and programmatic policies to prioritize investments in access to health care over policy solutions with the potential to affect entire communities. These investments provide extraordinary care for some but fail to provide real value when compared with other countries. The United States spends more than any other nation on medical care, $3.6 trillion,[5] but ranks 37th in overall health system performance worldwide.[6] While medical care accounts for only 20 percent of our health, it receives 90 percent of our heath care expenditures.[7] Of the remaining 80 percent, social conditions such as education, unemployment, poverty, environmental exposures, and community safety account for half.[7]

Our choices regarding food, schools, recreation, and other key health determinants are shaped by the choices available to us. People who live in concentrated impoverished areas with struggling schools and unsafe neighborhoods have vastly different experiences than their counterparts with stable incomes in thriving communities. These differences impact the health of individuals and populations in positive and negative ways. Yet, instead of examining these upstream influencers of health and addressing them with population-level strategies, the United States remains overly reliant on the health care system to deliver individually focused health solutions. Creating an equitable, healthy society will require a shift from our disproportionate focus on the individual to increased attention to systemic change through policy. While our individual choices—whether to smoke, exercise, or eat a healthy diet, for example—play a significant role in personal health outcomes, successful behavior change is rarely feasible without first changing the policy around environments, systems, and institutions. Policy is a strong enabler that makes the healthy choice the easy choice and creates laws, rules, regulations, and practices that promote health.

Think of it like being on a sinking ship. You need to bail the water (i.e., paying for medical services, focusing on access and insurance), but that does not solve your real problem (i.e., preventing illness in the first place). It only keeps you afloat—temporarily. You can only bail for so long before the boat sinks. US health care strategy prioritizes buying bigger and more buckets when instead we should be finding and fixing the hole (Figure 1-1).

Hospitals and health care systems are recognizing that patients' social circumstances impact their clinical outcomes. To improve patient outcomes, hospitals and health care systems are buying food, offering temporary housing, or covering transportation costs for high-risk patients. While such interventions may mitigate the acute social and economic challenges of individual patients, they provide no long-term solutions. These interventions are often limited to a small segment of the population—those who are in the worst health, have the greatest health care costs, or are enrolled in specific health insurance plans. Meanwhile, those patients who do not rank among the "sickest and most expensive" are ignored.

COVID-19 is mostly framed as a viral pandemic. It is probably better described, however, as a syndemic, defined as the aggregation of two or more concurrent or sequential epidemics or disease clusters in a population with biological interactions exacerbating the prognosis and burden of disease. We are not dealing with viral spread alone. We are also dealing with the effect of decades of neglectful social policies that have contributed

Note: Environmental, social, and community factors are negatively impacting population health. Despite this, solutions focus on expanding health care personnel and access, and meeting patients' immediate social needs.

Figure 1-1. Buy Bigger Buckets

to creating an environment where the virus could thrive. Those who are without paid sick leave, who do not earn a livable wage, and who endure housing and food insecurity shoulder a disproportionate burden of disease. Our nation needs to invest in our public health infrastructure, but that must be accompanied by policy changes that immediately address the societal vulnerabilities that have acutely exacerbated our experience with COVID-19 (Figure 1-2).

We need to stop buying buckets and start looking for the hole in the bottom of the boat. If we are to build vibrant, prosperous communities where people can live healthier,

Note: COVID-19 may have been the match, but a history of poor policy decisions resulting in disparities, inequities, and injustice provided plenty of kindling.

Figure 1-2. Just the Match

longer lives, we must advance policies that define people's opportunities to be healthy—increasing access to healthy food choices, early education, and green spaces. It is naive to think that programs and interventions can fix decades upon decades of racist and exclusionary state and federal laws. Only policy can fix what policy has broken. The advances we need to improve health and life expectancy will not come from a laboratory or clinic. They will come from legislatures, city councils, and other legislative and regulatory agencies, usually preceded by sustained community-based advocacy. For those who seek to improve health through policy change, this book is intended to be your companion. It is written by practitioners, elected officials, and other policymakers who have firsthand experience with the complex dynamics of policymaking through their professional careers. Its chapters share perspectives on the power of policy from the federal, state, and local levels; demonstrate several evidence-based policy packages developed by leading public health organizations; provide perspectives not only on legislative policy but on the roles of litigation and regulation; and reveal the existing threats to using policy to impact health. Although this book centers the stories of public health policy in urban communities, it can be a source of inspiration for professionals in all locales. Public health practitioners in urban and rural jurisdictions alike can benefit from the experiences shared by the authors as they seek to change policy where they are. Ultimately, our goal is to inspire current and future public health practitioners and policymakers to use policy to achieve optimal and equitable health for all.

REFERENCES

1. Centers for Disease Control and Prevention. Achievements in public health, 1900–1999: improvements in workplace safety—United States, 1900-1999. *MMWR*. 1999;48(22):461–9.

2. Centers for Disease Control and Prevention. Achievements in public health, 1900–1999 motor-vehicle safety: a 20th century public health achievement. *MMWR*. 1999;48(18):369–74.

3. Centers for Disease Control and Prevention. Achievements in public health, 1900–1999: tobacco use—United States, 1900–1999. *MMWR*. 1999;48(43):986–93.

4. Centers for Disease Control and Prevention. Ten greatest public health achievements–United States, 1900–1999. *MMWR*. 1999;48(12):241–3.

5. Abraham T. US healthcare spending estimated to grow to $3.6T this year. *Healthcare Dive*. May 29, 2019. Available at: https://www.healthcaredive.com/news/us-healthcare-spending-estimated-to-grow-to-36t-this-year/555658. Accessed November 10, 2020.

6. Murry CL, Frenk J. Ranking 37th–measuring the performance of the US health care system. *New Engl J Med*. 2010;362(2):98–9.

7. County Health Rankings and Roadmaps. 2020 county health rankings key findings report. March 2020. Available at: https://www.countyhealthrankings.org/reports/2020-county-health-rankings-key-findings-report. Accessed November 10, 2020.

THE POWER OF POLICY AT THE FEDERAL, STATE, AND LOCAL LEVELS

2

Federal Policy for Health

Edward L. Hunter, MA

Over 250 years go, Alexander Hamilton and other founders of the United States argued about the nature of their new nation's government. An important element of the debate was the struggle to define the relative powers of the levels of government and how to weave sovereign states together into a more perfect union. Generations after the Constitution was ratified, the argument endures: What are the roles of the central federal government, strong sovereign state governments, and other jurisdictions including counties, cities, and special districts? What kind of governments do we want, what do we expect from them, and what are the implications for advancing health-related policy?

The US health system reflects this continuing ambiguity, and understanding the dynamics is critical to pursuing effective policies to improve public health. America's founders couldn't have anticipated today's mosaic of policies and public health approaches and how they rest on diverse legal and financial entanglements that are constantly shifting in response to political and economic realities. This patchwork results in stark differences in the policies, programs, and public health capacity of communities across the United States, fosters power struggles as one level of government seeks to preempt action by others, and results in inequities in community health opportunities and outcomes. Paradoxically, while this environment fragments advocacy by public health professionals, it creates opportunities for policy experimentation and advancement.

There is no doubt that the federal government plays an essential and often dominant role in shaping policies that affect our health, making it a prime focus for public health advocacy. With the three branches of the federal government all having considerable levers of influence, many approaches exist for advancing the public's health:

1. Explicit powers enumerated in the US Constitution, including exclusive domain over borders and foreign affairs, broad powers to address matters that cross state lines (i.e., the basis for vast regulations of commercial activity), and promotion of the "general welfare" (i.e., the basis for broad programs and policies to improve health and its social determinants).

2. Sweeping ability to raise revenue through broad, adaptable taxes, and a largely unrestrained ability to spend money in ways determined by Congress. By contrast, most state and local government revenues are constrained by tax-base limitations, taxation

limits set by state constitutions or ballot initiatives, or requirements for balanced budgets, resulting in a comparative disadvantage in influence and leverage.

3. Constitutionally enshrined individual rights that supersede state powers and form the basis for policies that advance equity, such as the 14th Amendment's due process and equal protection clause,[1] which grounds many litigation strategies.

Though many perceive the federal government as all powerful, in reality key constraints affect choices of where to focus advocacy for health-related public policy. These constraints are both constitutional (e.g., states retain prerogatives in many areas, and the courts are often asked to protect those rights) and practical (e.g., political shifts result in pendulum swings between federal and state control, public- and private-sector influence, and even urban versus rural influence). Accordingly, the history of public health policy is full of examples of experimentation at the local level, the development of evidence of impact, and advocacy for adoption either in other jurisdictions or by the federal government. Most tobacco-control policy has followed this path. Over the past decade, for example, cities and then states banned the sale of tobacco products to anyone under the age of 21, supported by nationwide advocacy initiatives, which generated momentum for federal legislation enacted in 2019. At each level of government, tobacco policies have rested on different empowerments, including local licensing and regulatory authorities, state taxation authorities, and federal authority over interstate commerce and product safety. Even within individual levels of governments, strategies for advancing public health policy need to recognize how powers are divided across the executive, legislative, and judicial branches.

WHAT SHOULD PUBLIC HEALTH EXPECT FROM FEDERAL POLICY?

In pursuit of effective policies, where should public health advocates focus energy, and what should they expect from the federal government? Most fundamentally, we should expect all three branches of the national government to uphold their end of the grand compromise of federalism and use federal powers to advance public health in the following ways:

1. **Generating and sharing evidence for policy action at all levels**: Thomas Jefferson wrote that information is the most certain and most legitimate engine of government, and that freedom is the firstborn daughter of science. With its broad spending authority and its charge to promote general welfare, the federal government is uniquely capable of supporting the generation and sharing of data and research that inform policy debates across government and guide effective investments and interventions. At the same time, because of the federal government's broad influence and

spending in the health sector, it is particularly important for federal policies to set an effective framework for privacy and data sharing.

2. **Creating an environment that values public health science and protects scientific evidence from political influence**: There are many influences on policy, and public health advocates cannot expect science alone to dominate decision-making.* However, decision makers and the public need access to evidence that is free from political influence, and the public debate is best informed by science that can be trusted—whether it is ultimately followed or not. Policymakers need to assure the public that structures and safeguards are in place to prevent political considerations from influencing or "spinning" underlying scientific evidence.

3. **Acting as the ultimate "anchor institution" in its business practices**: As large employers and consumers in their communities, hospitals and businesses use their influence to promote health.[2] The federal government, which is in essence the nation's anchor institution, should use its influence in more focused ways. Its policies for workforce leave and benefits are the benchmark for other levels of government as well as unions and large employers. Its purchasing practices shape much of the economy. Adding a more explicit health strategy to federal business practices has strong potential for advancing health goals.

4. **Adopting tax policies that promote health equity and outcomes**: The federal government's broad tax powers have significant influence on individual and corporate health-related behavior. Examples of using the tax code to encourage health-related initiatives include deductible employer health programs, tax exemptions for charitable spending, community benefit spending requirements for tax-exempt hospitals, and earned income tax credits to alleviate poverty. The tax code can also be used to discourage unhealthy practices, as is the case with taxes on tobacco and alcohol. Federal policies can influence the practices of other levels of government. For example, the extent to which state taxes are deductible from federal taxes affects states' ability to sustain their own public health investments. Public health advocacy generally has focused on taxes to depress demand for unhealthy products, but there are other significant opportunities to reshape tax policy to advance public health goals.

5. **Prioritizing spending that promotes health equity and outcomes**: Rightfully, a great deal of public health advocacy has focused on spending for health-related programs, including direct public health spending and, to a lesser extent, social support programs like SNAP (i.e., the Supplemental Nutrition Assistance Program) that are subject to the annual appropriations process. Decisions on the allocation of

---

*Further reading is available at: "Politics and Public Health: Engaging the Third Rail"; https://journals.lww .com/jphmp/Fulltext/2016/09000/Politics_and_Public_Health_Engaging_the_Third_Rail.2.aspx.

health-related spending not only have practical effects but also demonstrate the extent to which we value equity and prioritize populations placed at risk, as the interconnectedness between economic and health risk is made more evident in our experience with the COVID-19 pandemic. Federal dollars can come with provisos and requirements, such as conditions for providers participating in Medicare, inclusion of mandatory benefits for health insurance plans with federal subsidies, and criteria attached to grants made available to state and local agencies. Each of these funding streams is a target for public health advocacy, with the expectation that the federal health "purse" be spent to maximize the public's health. Yet federal spending exceeds $4.4 trillion annually,[3] with only a fraction devoted to prevention and public health. Even proposals to re-invigorate public health infrastructure spending call for only $4 billion, with likely economic dividends that provide value back to the Treasury.[4] Beyond direct spending on health programs, federal spending spans all sectors—and advocates can pursue strategies that use all of the leverage this provides to improve health and health equity.

6. **Adopting policies that promote health in non-health federal programs**: The more we focus on social and economic factors that influence our health, the more important it is to advocate for effective federal policies across a broad spectrum. There have been episodic efforts—such as the National Prevention, Health Promotion, and Public Health Council established in 2010[5]—that possessed no direct authority but created a forum for federal agencies to consider policies that influence health. But the federal government needs an effective, continuing mechanism for understanding and addressing health-influencing policies outside the jurisdiction of health agencies. Many have called for local health officials to be "chief health strategists" for their communities.[6] We also need an empowered strategist at the federal level who can focus attention on policy change by systematically evaluating policies and programs for their health impact and bringing health-enhancing approaches to initiatives across government.

7. **Conducting a foreign policy that promotes health here and around the globe**: The federal government has exclusive responsibility for foreign affairs. To achieve public health goals, US foreign policy needs to be executed in a way that promotes global health and human rights and protects Americans from health threats that arise overseas. In parallel, public health goals require an immigration policy that both protects against the introduction of infectious diseases and promotes the health of new Americans.

8. **Regulating commerce to protect against harm**: Another unambiguous federal responsibility is the regulation of interstate commerce. This provides the basis for activities such as regulating unhealthy products sold across state lines, providing for the safety and efficacy of drugs, and protecting the environment. Congressional

action to establish federal regulatory power is inhibited more by political will (including both ideological and economic considerations) than by Constitutional limits. Legislation is only the beginning of the story. Typically, Congress provides broad direction to the executive branch, which is expected to promulgate detailed rules. As a result, regulations are particularly sensitive to political swings—for example, as a new administration takes power after a presidential election—and, because they are often revisited, they are a key focus for public health advocacy.

9. **Modeling a focus on prevention and social determinants of health in federal health benefits programs**: With the federal government providing most of the nation's financing for health care, federal coverage and payment rules for Medicare, Medicaid, and other programs have a large influence on the balance of spending between upstream prevention and downstream treatment. Shifting toward greater investment in prevention and social determinants requires short-term steps, such as making better use of the flexibility of Medicaid and Medicare Advantage to enable plans to address social needs that inhibit positive patient health outcomes.[7,8] It also requires longer-term initiatives that move the overall health system further upstream, such as enabling federal programs to participate in multisector collaborations that address the social determinants of health and prioritizing spending on public health infrastructure.

10. **Using courts to protect rights and uphold due process**: Public health advocates seeking broad policy gains often turn to federal courts as a powerful complement to legislative and executive action. Courts protect individual rights under the Constitution, protect against executive action beyond the parameters of authority granted by Congress, and protect against actions that violate due process requirements, as in the Administrative Procedures Act.[9] For example, public health advocates have sought court intervention to preserve environmental regulations and pursued litigation to prevent the introduction of work requirements to the Medicaid program. With a divided electorate that often results in a divided government, it is increasingly important for public health advocates to gain skill and experience in litigation. Advocates can also focus attention on agencies that shape US government positions in pending litigation, including the Department of Justice and the Office of Management and Budget.

Given the federal government's power and reach, there are enormous opportunities to advance public health goals at the federal level. As public health advocates seek to broaden their influence in addressing upstream factors affecting our health, they need to view the federal government through a broad lens, addressing the full range of policy levers, seeking skills and partnerships to take advantage of opportunities, and expanding expectations for effective use of federal policy.

REFERENCES

1. National Archives. The Constitution of the United States: a transcription. Available at: https://www.archives.gov/founding-docs/constitution-transcript. Accessed April 23, 2020.

2. Democracy Collaborative. Leveraging anchor institutions. Available at: https://democracycollaborative.org/learn/collections/leveraging-anchor-institutions. Accessed April 23, 2020.

3. US Department of the Treasury. Your guide to America's finances. Available at: https://datalab.usaspending.gov/americas-finance-guide. Accessed April 23, 2020.

4. DeSalvo K, Parekh A, Hoagland GW, Dilley A, Kaiman S, Hines M, Levi J. Developing a financing system to support public health infrastructure. *Am J Public Health*. 2019; 109(10):1358–61.

5. National Prevention Council. National Prevention Council Action Plan. Implementing the National Prevention Strategy. June 2012. Available at: https://www.improvingpopulationhealth.org/Action%20Plan.pdf. Accessed April 23, 2020.

6. Public Health Leadership Forum. The Department of Health and Human Services as the nation's chief health strategist: transforming public health and health care to create healthy communities. Available at: https://www.resolve.ngo/docs/dhhs-as-the-nations-chief-health-strategist-color636869420833360430.pdf. Accessed April 23, 2020

7. National Alliance to Impact the Social Determinants of Health. Getting to health and well-being for the nation: a call for cross-sector action to impact the social determinants of health. September 2018. Available at: https://www.nasdoh.org/wp-content/uploads/2018/09/NASDOH-White-Paper.pdf. Accessed April 23, 2020.

8. National Alliance to Impact the Social Determinants of Health. Supporting state innovation in Medicaid: policies for addressing social determinants of health. April 2019. Available at: https://www.nasdoh.org/wp-content/uploads/2019/04/Medicaid-Leave-Behind_Final.pdf. Accessed April 23, 2020.

9. US Environmental Protection Agency. Summary of the Administrative Procedure Act. Available at: https://www.epa.gov/laws-regulations/summary-administrative-procedure-act. Accessed April 23, 2020.

3

The Adverse Impact of Federal Health Policies on Health, Migration, and the Economy: The Case of Puerto Rico

Maria Levis-Peralta, MPH, MPA, PCMH-CCE and
Grace Guerrero Ramirez, MSPH

THE TERRITORIAL PENALTY: DISPARATE FEDERAL HEALTH POLICIES FOR THE ARCHIPELAGO

Puerto Ricans have been US citizens since 1917, but the island's status as a territory restricts the rights of all who live there. A Puerto Rican who lives in one of the 50 US states is afforded the same rights as all US citizens, including full access to health benefits such as Medicare, Medicaid, Supplemental Security Income, and other social programs. However, if any US citizen chooses to live in Puerto Rico, federal policy imposes significant limitations and caps on health and social service funding. This may explain why Puerto Rico hosts some of the highest rates of poverty and chronic disease compared to the states. It also helps explain why Puerto Rico has experienced a fierce out-migration over the past decade. From 2010 to 2017, 458,000 people migrated from the island to one of the 50 US states.[1]

Puerto Rico's underfunded Medicare and Medicaid programs and the delays in disbursement of federal disaster relief and emergency funds are just some examples from a broad swath of policies that negatively impact health and economics in Puerto Rico.

MEDICARE UNDERFUNDING: IMPLICATIONS FOR AN AGING POPULATION

Disparate Medicare funding has serious implications for Puerto Rico's aging population. Low-income residents (i.e., those living below 200% of the federal poverty level) in Puerto Rico who have contributed to Medicare their entire life through payroll deductions receive Medicare Advantage coverage that is 43% less than the US national average and 39% less than the state with the lowest coverage.[2] However, if they decide to emigrate to one of the 50 US states, they will receive full Medicare Advantage coverage according to the state where they choose to live. Additionally, they can receive Supplemental Security Income, which pays benefits to disabled adults and children who have limited resources, a low-income subsidy, which assists in paying their prescription drug coverage, and other subsidies for which they would be ineligible if they lived in Puerto Rico.

These circumstances create perverse incentives that fuel the exodus of people, particularly the most vulnerable and poor, from Puerto Rico. After the 2017 hurricanes and during the COVID-19 pandemic, enrollment decreased for the Medicare Advantage "Dual Eligible" Program in which most low-income Medicare beneficiaries in Puerto Rico are enrolled.[3] This suggests that poor elderly citizens are either migrating, not recertifying for Medicaid, or dying at rates higher than expected.

THE MEDICAID CLIFF: A LOOMING FUNDING DISASTER

The Medicaid program, which covers approximately 43% of Puerto Rico's population,[4,5] also suffers from poor federal funding. Key differences between the Medicaid program in Puerto Rico and elsewhere can be summarized as follows:

1. **Federal funding for Puerto Rico's Medicaid program is capped.** The federal government must cover at least 50% of what each state spends on its Medicaid program. This is known as the federal medical assistance percentage (FMAP). The FMAP for Puerto Rico is set at 55%. However, Puerto Rico does not automatically receive that amount because its federal funding is capped well below the full cost of the program. From 1999 to 2011, Puerto Rico received funding at a FMAP of 17%, significantly below the 50% FMAP minimum for the 50 US states. This leaves Puerto Rico with significant expenses to cover. In fact, Puerto Rico spent more from 1999 to 2011 to cover the local share of its health insurance program (the portion not covered by the federal government) than its total debt before interest. Put simply, Puerto Rico could have significantly reduced its fiscal deficit if its Medicaid assistance from the federal government were not capped.

   Puerto Rico often has peered over the "Medicaid cliff," a euphemism for the prospect of losing the majority of funding necessary for the program. Every two to three years, Congress appropriates funding specifically to offset the difference between the Medicaid funding cap and the FMAP in order to ensure Medicaid's financial feasibility in Puerto Rico. Since 2017, the FMAP has increased considerably, but these temporary fixes create continuity problems for revenue projections. This reduces Puerto Rico's capacity to carry out much-needed long-term planning to transform its health system.

2. **The income eligibility threshold is much lower in Puerto Rico.** Many people in Puerto Rico who live in poverty may not qualify for Medicaid. Puerto Rico uses a local poverty level to establish income-based Medicaid eligibility. Under this threshold, a family of four would be eligible for Medicaid with an annual gross income lower than $10,200. This is approximately 40% of the federal poverty level,[6] equivalent to a

$25,750 eligibility cap for a family of four in one of the 50 US states in 2019. Furthermore, the federal government recently required applicants to use modified adjusted gross income to calculate household size and income. This makes it more difficult for people in Puerto Rico to enroll in the program. The Government of Puerto Rico is proposing changes to make Medicaid eligibility and enrollment more similar to what is seen in the 50 US states.

3. **Health care providers are paid less.** Reimbursement rates for Medicaid providers in Puerto Rico are significantly lower than those for Medicaid providers in the 50 US states and other territories, fueling a "brain drain" as physicians are consistently offered work where reimbursement is higher. Therefore, low Medicaid payment rates in Puerto Rico likely contribute to provider shortages, poor access to certain specialty services, and lengthy wait times.[7]

Disparities in health care funding create a situation that is unfair and unsustainable. As Puerto Rico faces multiple crises, it is essential to advocate for sustainable and equitable solutions.

FEDERAL EMERGENCY AND DISASTER RELIEF FUNDING

The devastating blow of Hurricanes Irma and Maria in 2017 increased the needs of an already impoverished population and stressed an already burdened health and social services infrastructure. Federal and local responses to these disasters offer opportunities to understand the impact of different approaches to funding public health work in Puerto Rico.

On one hand, the process for the disbursement of $19.9 billion that Congress appropriated through the Department of Housing and Urban Development (HUD) has been significantly delayed. These long-term recovery and mitigation funds are needed to address pressing social, housing, and infrastructure needs and to revitalize the economy. As of 2020, three years after the hurricanes, HUD had disbursed only a fraction of the funding. The agency missed crucial deadlines, citing concerns with Puerto Rico's government. Meanwhile, people replaced the roofs on their houses with blue tarps, and public infrastructure continued to decay. On April 19, 2021 HUD announced the disbursement of the remaining funds approved nearly two years ago. The agency also announced the removal of conditions and restrictions that limited Puerto Rico's access to and use of the funds.[8]

On the other hand, the Centers for Disease Control and Prevention increased its presence in Puerto Rico, providing significant technical assistance and partnering with the Puerto Rico Department of Health to identify public health needs and deploy funding and human resources. This last approach has been vital in strengthening Puerto Rico's public health infrastructure.

Unfortunately, the response to COVID-19 has once again revealed disparities in funding for public health and health care. Although there is significant need, Puerto Rico received a substantially lower amount of relief funds through the CARES Act compared with other jurisdictions. Specifically, the formulas the federal government used to distribute the funding did not take into account Puerto Rico's population, putting health providers in Puerto Rico at a severe disadvantage compared with those in the 50 US states.

RECOMMENDATIONS

Federal funding caps and unequal treatment for health and human services directly impact the Puerto Rican government's finances and disproportionately affect Puerto Rico's most vulnerable residents. By providing a permanent solution for Medicaid parity (including the elimination of funding caps) and ensuring that all Medicare premiums and reimbursements are comparable to those in the 50 US states, Congress can provide long-term relief. At the same time, these measures will enable Congress to address some of the causes of the Puerto Rican government's high deficits by providing stable revenue projections necessary for planning the transformation of the local health system. Similar measures should be taken to provide parity for Puerto Rico in other health and social services programs, including programs for telehealth capabilities, and to offset health care providers' losses resulting from shelter-at-home policies and patients' fear of contagion during the COVID-19 pandemic. These policies will help reverse health disparities and improve Puerto Rico's fiscal situation.

In addition, both Congress and the Administration should eliminate the systematic exclusion of Puerto Rico from many national statistics. Because these statistics inform funding formulas, Puerto Rico's exclusion makes the island more likely to be left out of funding opportunities.

These policies, combined with a package of local and federal actions aimed at restoring economic growth and increasing transparency and accountability, can help deter out-migration and steer Puerto Rico out of its current crisis.

CONCLUSION

While it is easy for Congress, and in some instances correct, to place responsibility on local politicians for Puerto Rico's woes, federal actions are also responsible for the archipelago's current crisis. Federal policymakers fear that a long-term solution will be expensive, but the cost of inaction may be higher. Without a permanent solution to federal funding disparities, it is practically impossible for the government of Puerto Rico to engage in long-term planning efforts necessary to transform its local health system. This transformation requires up-front investment, which is currently unavailable to the local government due to the debt crisis and the lack of alternatives for financing. The federal government has the opportunity and the moral imperative to provide Puerto Rico with equitable funding to address the urgent health needs and enable the long-term prosperity of its people.

REFERENCES

1. Puerto Rico Institute of Statistics. Little more than 2% of the population emigrated in 2017 [Poco más del 2% de la población emigró en el 2017]. 2019. Available at: https://estadisticas .pr/files/Inventario/publicaciones/CP_PM2017_8_23_2019_FINAL.pdf. Accessed May 28, 2020.

2. Mújica-Trenche HA. Healthcare reform developments in Puerto Rico. 2018. Available at: https://assets.hcca-info.org/Portals/0/PDFs/Resources/Conference_Handouts/Regional_ Conference/2018/puerto-rico/Mujicaprint2.pdf. Accessed May 28, 2020.

3. Centers for Medicare and Medicaid Services. Medicare Advantage/Part D contract and enroll-ment data. 2020. Available at: https://www.cms.gov/Research-Statistics-Data-and-Systems/ Statistics-Trends-and-Reports/MCRAdvPartDEnrolData/index. Accessed June 1, 2020.

4. Statistics April 2021. Government of Puerto Rico Medicaid program. Available at: https:// www.medicaid.pr.gov/Info/Statistics. Accessed May 9, 2021.

5. US Census Bureau. Numeric and Percent change in resident population of the 50 states, the District of Columbia, and Puerto Rico: 2020 census and 2010 census. https://www2.census .gov/programs-surveys/decennial/2020/data/apportionment/apportionment-2020-tableE .pdf. Accessed May 9, 2021.

6. Buderi K. Mandated report: Medicaid in Puerto Rico. Medicaid and CHIP Payment and Access Commission. 2018. Available at: https://www.macpac.gov/wp-content/ uploads/2018/10/Mandated-Report-Medicaid-in-Puerto-Rico.pdf. Accessed May 28, 2020.

7. Solomon J. Puerto Rico's Medicaid program needs an ongoing commitment of federal funds. Center on Budget and Policy Priorities. 2019. Available at: https://www.cbpp.org/research/ health/puerto-ricos-medicaid-program-needs-an-ongoing-commitment-of-federal-funds#_ ftn15. Accessed May 28, 2020.

8. National Low Income Housing Coalition. HUD releases full housing mitigation funding to Puerto Rico. 2021. Available at: https://nlihc.org/resource/hud-releases-full-housing-mitigation-funding-puerto-rico-inspector-general-reports. Accessed May 3, 2021.

4

The State Perspective

John Auerbach, MBA and Monica Valdes Lupi, JD, MPH

EVOLUTION OF STATE HEALTH OFFICIALS AS CHIEF HEALTH STRATEGISTS

In the governmental public health system, state health departments play a critical role in advancing policies that protect, promote, and improve population health. Among the specialized roles of such departments are cross-jurisdictional epidemiology and laboratory services, funding and implementing statewide educational initiatives and preventive services, developing and enforcing environmental protections, and preventing and responding to emergencies of all kinds. Such departments routinely support the work of local health departments with funding and, particularly when local departments are small and have limited surge capacity, with direct assistance. In addition, state public health departments advise and support elected officials in the consideration of various policies, laws, and regulations, not infrequently gaining new responsibilities as a result of subsequent actions.[1]

While a wide range of responsibilities have long fallen under the purview of state health departments, the nature of the work has evolved over time. Functions and roles have changed significantly since the turn of the century. After the terrorist attacks on September 11, 2001, a new and major component of health departments' work involved responding to emerging threats to the general public; recent examples include climate change, vaping, the opioid epidemic, and a series of deadly novel viruses. Occasional short-term infusions of specialized funding addressed urgent matters, but, in general, core public health funding peaked in 2008 and has declined since then.[2] When the Affordable Care Act was passed in 2010, making health insurance available for millions of Americans who previously relied on public health departments for some of their care, many state public health departments responded by scaling back their clinical services.

Amid these changes, different concepts have emerged for how public health departments should adapt and plan for the future—for example, assuming the role of Chief Health Strategist (CHS) and expanding their vision as a move toward Public Health 3.0.[3] Both approaches are intended to help support health departments in accelerating innovation to respond to current and future conditions. They share common elements such as guiding action with up-to-date and sophisticated data, working in close partnership with the health information technology and non-health sectors, using the latest evidence and science, and developing policies that promote optimal health for all. At the start of a new decade already filled with public health challenges, it is worth examining just how much state public health practice has evolved. Is the work of state public health departments fundamentally different than it was 10 or 20 years ago?

THE POWER OF STATE HEALTH POLICY

Two policy-related essential health services that fall under the state health department include: (1) "create, champion, and implement policies, plans, and laws that impact health;" and (2) "utilize legal and regulatory actions designed to improve and protect the public's health."[4] State health departments possess a powerful ability to impact health through broad, systems-based approaches and diverse policy levers. Consider, for example, the emergency declarations many states used during the H1N1 outbreak in 2009–2010 to expand those who could administer vaccines, and during the ongoing opioid epidemic to limit inappropriate prescribing. Additionally, state health departments can at times promulgate important regulations aimed at protecting the public's health, such as those involving immunizations for infectious diseases and tobacco-control regulations. As such, state health departments have the capacity to develop, implement, and evaluate policies.

LEVERAGING ALTERNATIVE DATA SOURCES TO ADVANCE COLLECTIVE ACTIVITIES

For decades, public health has disproportionately relied on information sources such as data for reportable infectious diseases, birth and death reports, and surveys of the general public as well as certain subpopulations. Examples of traditional data collection and use can be found in the state health departments' oversight of public health preparedness, vaccination, and disease surveillance. Public health departments developed these data systems to ensure that the information being collected is accurate, timely, and actionable.

More recently, using the Public Health 3.0 and CHS approaches, many state health departments also use nontraditional data sources, often to provide insights into the social, economic, and environmental factors that affect health. For example, in Massachusetts the Department of Public Health was able to link nearly 20 different state databases relevant to the opioid epidemic while still protecting confidentiality. Through this new data platform, the department identified populations at highest need for services—such as postpartum women and individuals experiencing homelessness or being discharged from correctional facilities—and garnered millions of dollars in new state funding to support targeted treatment programs.

DEVELOPING INNOVATIVE POLICIES TO RESPOND TO PUBLIC HEALTH CRISES

Public health will always need to adapt its traditional approaches to new problems that arise. Greater collaboration across sectors has enabled public health organizations with limited resources to evolve. In the wake of lung illnesses associated with the use of e-cigarettes, for example, state health departments have been on the front lines working with elected officials, community partners, and other key stakeholders to respond with innovative policies.

In January 2020, New Jersey enacted legislation banning the sale of all flavored e-cigarettes. In 2019, eight states—Massachusetts, Michigan, Montana, New York, Oregon, Rhode Island, Utah, and Washington—took emergency action to temporarily ban the sale of flavored e-cigarettes. These laws were challenged by those with vested interests, as is the case in many instances where state public health departments take action to protect the public.

State health departments have also been leaders in responding to the opioid misuse and addiction crisis. Leveraging evidence-based approaches, cutting-edge surveillance tools, and collaboration with health partners and the private sector, they have success-fully launched policies that expand access to lifesaving overdose-reversal medications and syringe service programs. These include efforts in Virginia in 2016 where, following the declaration of the opioid crisis as a public health emergency, the state passed new public health laws to provide prescribers with the authority to allow an individual to administer naloxone without the prescriber's knowledge of the patient being treated. Virginia also expanded Good Samaritan protections. States like Vermont, Rhode Island, and Pennsylvania have led the way in developing state policies to expand access to medication-assisted treatment and mental health parity, to ensure that people with substance-use disorders could access comprehensive treatment and services.

ADVANCING HEALTH EQUITY AND ADDRESSING THE SOCIAL DETERMINANTS OF HEALTH

Public health departments have long developed initiatives for populations who are at disproportionate risk. From efforts to reduce higher rates of mortality among Black infants to HIV prevention services for gay and transgender people to vaccination cam-paigns targeted to older adults, public health has a tradition of serving those with the greatest need.

For data and analysis on the persistent racial and ethnic health inequities across key health conditions, many organizations and individuals across the country rely on their state health department to issue reports and policy briefs. However, public health efforts to address health inequities have too often been limited to perceptions of which roles are within the sector's domain: screening, education, behavioral change interventions, and health services.

In the CHS/Public Health 3.0 era, the focus has increasingly shifted to encompass the social, economic, and environmental conditions that affect health and antiracism initiatives. Health departments have received greater recognition for their potential to advance health equity and craft creative policies that go beyond addressing specific social needs by focusing on structural and systemic racism. Partners turn to state health departments not only as conveners but also to address root causes.

Several states have implemented public health strategies that strengthen community engagement and support resilience frameworks that build on community assets. Examples include Rhode Island's Health Equity Zones and Maryland's Health Enterprise Zones (HEZ).[5,6] In these states, the health departments have developed policies that promote community-driven, place-based solutions to reduce health disparities and improve health outcomes. The Maryland model offers a tax credit incentive for "HEZ Practitioners" focused on locales with the sharpest inequities.

State health departments have also responded to adverse childhood experiences by designing programs and training staff on trauma-informed care. California has launched nontraditional approaches led by state Surgeon General Nadine Burke-Harris, an expert in addressing adverse childhood experiences (ACEs). In December 2020, Dr. Burke-Harris released a blueprint to address ACEs that called for a cross-sector approach focusing on changing policies and practices to address toxic stress and racism.[7]

Finally, the state health department in Florida has piloted an initiative to create Age-Friendly Public Health with the goal of improving older adults' health by adapting existing programs, gathering targeted data, and working in partnerships with other sectors. These examples demonstrate new and creative ways for public health proponents to address upstream factors to improve health.

CONCLUSION

State health departments have played and will continue to play crucial roles in protecting the health of the public. With new health risks and an increased number of emergencies, these departments have changed accordingly. Despite a lack of adequate resources, more and more state health departments have adopted CHS/Public Health 3.0 approaches. By leveraging data systems, responding creatively to public health crises and emerging trends, and building on the strength of the communities they serve to advance health equity, state public health departments and their employees have shown public health's continued ability to be relevant, effective, and invaluable to the people of the United States.

REFERENCES

1. Association of State and Territorial Health Officials. Profile of state public health, volume two. 2011. Available at: https://www.astho.org/Profile/Volume-Two/. Accessed April 2, 2020.

2. Trust For America's Health. The impact of chronic underfunding of America's public health system: trends, risks, and recommendations. 2019. Available at: https://www.tfah.org/report-details/2019-funding-report/. Accessed April 2, 2020.

3. DeSalvo KB, Wang YC, Harris A, et al. Public health 3.0: a call to action for public health to meet the challenges of the 21st century. *Prev Chronic Dis.* 2017;14.

4. 10 Essential Public Health Services Futures Initiative Task Force. 10 essential public health services. September 2020. Available at: https://phnci.org/uploads/resource-files/EPHS-English.pdf. Accessed September 30, 2020.

5. State of Rhode Island Department of Health. Health Equity Zones (HEZ) Initiative. Available at: https://health.ri.gov/programs/detail.php?pgm_id=1108. Accessed April 2, 2020.

6. Association of State and Territorial Health Officials. Maryland fights health disparities with Health Enterprise Zones legislation. 2014. Available at: https://www.astho.org/health-equity/md-health-enterprise-zone-story. Accessed April 2, 2020.

7. Bhushan D, Kotz K, McCall J, et al. Roadmap for resilience: the California Surgeon General's report on adverse childhood experiences, toxic stress, and health. Office of the California Surgeon General, 2020.

5

From the Roots Up: The Critical Role of Local Action in Policy Change

Colleen Bridger, MPH, PhD and Ron Nirenberg, MA

Rarely is local government fortunate enough to have a mayor and local health director who share the same commitment to and vision for addressing the root causes of poor public health outcomes. In January 2018, San Antonio became the first city in Texas to raise to 21 the legal age to purchase tobacco, more than a year before the legal age was raised statewide. This hard-won accomplishment was a victory for public health and millions of young people who are especially vulnerable to the harms of tobacco.

CityHealth is a national program that identifies evidence-based policy-level interventions such as Tobacco 21 and awards medals to cities based on their levels of implementation. CityHealth provided us a framework to use as we worked together to make meaningful policy changes addressing public health in San Antonio. Our city went from having no medal in 2017 to a gold medal—the highest honor given by CityHealth—just two years later. This is how we got here and what other cities can learn from our experience.

SET THE FOUNDATION FOR PARTNERSHIP

San Antonio has had clear public health priorities with strong support for addressing straightforward health issues, including reducing rates of teenage pregnancy, diabetes, and obesity, among others. Tobacco use and vaping and the need for prevention, however, had not received the same level of attention. In spring 2017, San Antonio elected a new mayor and hired a new health director. At our first meeting we quickly agreed to work together on multiple public health priorities, and Tobacco 21 was at the top of the list.

We knew Tobacco 21 would not pass in San Antonio without both public health science and political advocacy. With the support of the mayor's office, the health director focused on the science, telling elected officials what they needed to know and, just as important, what they did not want to hear. The health director worked with public health advocates at the city, state, and national levels to orchestrate the advocacy and education campaign. Meanwhile, the mayor reinforced the need to "follow the science" with members of the city council and worked with the business community to help them understand why Tobacco 21 was essential for a healthy workforce and lower health care costs. With these roles and responsibilities, we used our respective skills and experience to help San Antonio lead in the burgeoning state and national Tobacco 21 movement. We knew that if San Antonio could succeed, those who feared to try would have no excuse, and we took pride in the occasional comment, "Well, if San Antonio can pass Tobacco 21, anybody can."

GET ADVOCATES ON THE SAME PAGE

Even when working toward the same goal, advocates may not have the same views about the best path forward. Making sure that all advocates are on the same page is an essential first step to avoid the infighting that impedes progress. We encountered this issue when determining the pace at which to pursue Tobacco 21. Local advocates had unsuccessfully tried to get Tobacco 21 legislation introduced during the previous legislative session. They feared that continuing their efforts in a year when the legislature was adjourned (the Texas legislature convenes every other year) could undo the momentum they had achieved and possibly lead to legislation that preempted all Texas cities from enacting Tobacco 21. We supported a more expedited approach and swayed the advocates with a bit of stubbornness, some political courage, a collective sense of urgency, and increasing support from national tobacco-control leaders.

USE DATA TO YOUR ADVANTAGE

Communicating about policy requires that advocates connect the science with real stories that are happening in the community and ways policy will improve people's lives. We began by explaining to local elected officials the addiction rates for tobacco users under age 21 and the positive impact of preventing younger people from buying and accessing tobacco products. We connected the issue to their constituents with hot-off-the-press polling data indicating that San Antonians were ready for Tobacco 21. Three-quarters of city residents approved of Tobacco 21, mirroring state and national sentiments.

But data alone are never enough. Storytelling from real people can put statistics into context and make them more compelling. City council members heard from teenagers, children of people who had passed away from long-term tobacco use, and medical professionals who treated people for long-term tobacco use. A young pillar of the local business community, who at the time chaired the largest chamber of commerce in San Antonio, testified about how his parents had died because of tobacco use and how that affected his childhood.

USE ALL AVAILABLE RESOURCES

We had tremendous help from influential partners in the health sector, including CityHealth, the Campaign for Tobacco-Free Kids, the American Cancer Society, the American Heart Association, and the University of Texas MD Anderson Cancer Center. One of the most beneficial modes of support was hiring an influencer to counter the arguments of an anti-Tobacco 21 lobbyist. Having an ally to help us craft our messaging, devise strategy, and even tip us off about who would run into whom at the holiday party was invaluable.

Those of us in public health need to do a better job of utilizing the strengths and skills of lobbyists. The implementation of public health policy cannot rely on science alone, no matter how solid. For Tobacco 21 in San Antonio, we used the same rules that the tobacco industry has used for decades, with elected officials receiving the same amount of information from and the same level of interaction with our side. Too often, meager anti-tobacco resources have been overpowered by the tobacco lobby, enabling them to drown out our critical messages. The speed with which we acted, the comprehensive nature of our approach, and our lobbyist's counter-messaging neutralized pro-tobacco efforts.

IDENTIFY CHAMPIONS

San Antonio is a diverse, collaborative city that welcomes cross-sector collaboration, so we were able to find champions within a range of constituencies. We leveraged the mayor's relationships throughout the city to rally support behind Tobacco 21 and identify other potential supporters. We worked with the business community and others to build awareness of tobacco control as a public health priority and to develop the necessary political fortitude among our colleagues at City Hall. Several council members were particularly enthusiastic about Tobacco 21—with encouragement, they never missed an opportunity to speak in favor of the policy. Key members of our business community, led by the largest chamber of commerce in the city, used their political influence with elected officials. Chambers had been extremely powerful advocates—and sometimes leaders—of the Tobacco 21 movement in other cities, so we quickly enlisted their support in San Antonio.

Nevertheless, we knew the vocal minority would show up at city council meetings and in council members' offices, so our San Antonio Tobacco 21 coalition made sure we outnumbered, out-educated, and out-performed them. On days when hearings were held and votes were taken for Tobacco 21, we ensured that the council chambers were filled with our allies in the fight. We equipped these teens, veterans, business owners, moms, dads, and others with San Antonio Tobacco 21 shirts, buttons, signs, and well-prepared arguments. Knowing that optics are important, we wanted to convey the message that the majority of people in the city supported positive change.

COUNTER FALSE NARRATIVES

We encountered one persistent narrative: that smoking regulations in Texas had not met wide political approval. Historically, that has not been true, either in the state or in San Antonio. In the previous decade, San Antonio had implemented various tobacco-control measures, including bans on smoking indoors and in public parks.

Even so, not everyone thought that Tobacco 21 was right for San Antonio or Texas. Here in Military City USA, we confronted the argument that those who die for our country should be allowed to smoke before age 21. Our counter-argument: We should do better for our service members by protecting them from an addictive substance that changes brain structure. National data showing the challenges faced by military recruits who are smokers and testimony from veterans' groups helped us get our point across.

The argument of personal liberty resonates strongly in San Antonio. We explained to detractors that protecting public health is not an infringement on freedom and that Tobacco 21 in no way eliminates personal choice. Fortunately, many youth in our community agreed with this perspective. We enlisted young people who could talk to the issue and took every public speaking opportunity to explain that personal freedoms are not at stake, but that health is.

Convenience store operators, for whom cigarette sales are an important portion of revenue, posed another challenge. They argued that Tobacco 21 would put them out of business. People under age 21 could simply walk across the street to purchase tobacco in one of the nearly 30 small cities within the metropolitan area with their own rules. To quell their fears, we presented them with research showing that other cities had passed Tobacco 21 legislation with no detriment to local business. We addressed their apprehension about competing stores in adjacent jurisdictions with a promise that we would pursue Tobacco 21 at the state level once it was implemented in San Antonio. We held true to that promise: Tobacco 21 passed statewide a year later.

Like all advocates for important public health policy, we had detractors and a vocal, if minority, opposition. We countered their false narratives with consistent, science-based responses delivered by compelling, relevant messengers like military veterans, youth, and cancer survivors. When some opponents showed up on the day of the vote, the majority of city council members knew enough about the science behind our effort and were empowered enough by our advocacy efforts to feel confident in voting "yes." We should note that a lawsuit filed against the City of San Antonio claimed that we did not have authority at the local level to pass this ordinance. When Texas passed statewide Tobacco 21 legislation, that legal challenge became moot.

NEVER UNDERESTIMATE THE POWER OF LOCAL POLICY

Seeing what Tobacco 21 has accomplished in San Antonio, the State of Texas, and now throughout the country, we cannot understate the significance of one local government making a difference on a public health priority. San Antonio adopted Tobacco 21 in a state where one party, the Republican Party, has controlled every branch of government for almost three decades. We believe San Antonio became a tipping point in a progressive, science-driven national effort that has saved countless lives from the harms of tobacco. We have seen that policy enacted at the local level can be just as influential, and just as effective, as policy enacted at the state and federal levels.

Those who want to follow our example need to begin with a strong relationship between science and public policy. We've seen the importance of following the science while developing public health policy magnified in our current response to the COVID-19 pandemic. Policymakers should value and protect public health officials' autonomy to use scientific facts to drive a bold public health agenda. Public health officials should prioritize collaboration that ensures policymakers take those priorities to heart and instills a sense of responsibility among all members of government to improve lives. It is a formula that San Antonio has demonstrated can lead to positive change.

II

EXISTING POLICY TOOLS AND FRAMEWORKS

6

The CityHealth Framework

Catherine Patterson, MPP and Grace Castillo, MPH

We all deserve to live the healthiest possible life. From the food we eat to the places we live to how we get around, health begins in our homes and communities and at our jobs and schools. But the opportunity to live healthily is not uniformly distributed; it is, in fact, shaped by systemic inequities. People who live in concentrated impoverished areas with struggling schools and unsafe neighborhoods have vastly different opportunities than those who live in thriving communities and have stable incomes. The rain falls on each of us equally, but only those with access to an umbrella can stay dry.

This health opportunity gap has been on display throughout the COVID-19 pandemic. The burden of the virus falls disproportionately on Black, Latinx, and Indigenous people[1] and has brought to the fore issues such as systemic racism and structural inequities. The consequences of the economic disruption caused by COVID-19, including increased evictions, food insecurity, and joblessness, are likely to be disproportionately shouldered by the "working poor" and people of color.[2] Policy has created and exacerbated these inequities, and policy must be utilized to fix these transgressions.

UNDERSTANDING SOCIAL DETERMINANTS AND SOCIAL NEEDS

Until the community conditions in which people live are changed, progress toward improving people's health will be slow. Before COVID-19, there was increasing interest in the medical community's role in addressing social factors and their impact on patient outcomes. However, these efforts focused primarily on a patient's immediate and specific social needs rather than on improving broader community conditions.[3] Social needs are focused on the individual and mediated at the individual level (e.g., eating better, remediating the mold in an individual's apartment). By contrast, social determinants work at the community and systems level.

In 2008, the World Health Organization defined social determinants as "conditions in which people are born, grow, live, work, and age" and "the fundamental drivers of these conditions."[4] This definition prioritizes a broad, community-wide focus on the underlying social and economic conditions in which people live rather than on the immediate needs of any one individual. Buying food, offering temporary housing, and covering ride-share programs are less expensive than providing repeat health care services for the highest-cost patients, but this individually focused assistance does not improve the underlying social and economic factors that affect the health of everyone in a community. The demand for these and other interventions to address social needs are driven by the absence of critical resources in a community. While there are short-term economic gains in mediating the social needs of a patient, real progress toward improving community and economic conditions and reducing health disparities requires policy, legislative, and regulatory change.

There is no question that policy has a major influence on health. As just one example, policies that increase the price of cigarettes have curbed tobacco use. Procurement policies can make healthy foods more readily available. In turn, ease of access can incentivize people to make smarter decisions about nutrition. Policies can require elementary schools to offer physical education or new infrastructure projects to provide access to biking and walking trails. Landlord and property management policies that mandate regular maintenance and building updates can reduce asthma triggers and lead sources. However, given the universe of policies that purport to improve health, it can be overwhelming to choose the right interventions for these complex problems. CityHealth, an initiative of the de Beaumont Foundation and Kaiser Permanente, was created to identify the most effective local policy solutions to make communities healthier, more vibrant, and more productive places to live.

WHAT IS CITYHEALTH?

CityHealth helps cities attain better outcomes for their residents by advancing a menu of proven policies that improve people's day-to-day health, well-being, and quality of life. CityHealth targets city-level policy change because cities are where innovative solutions are born, tested, and proven. City officials, frequently at the forefront of emerging challenges, are swift and highly skilled in adopting new policies—often despite state and federal gridlock. Sound policies can also help cities attract families who want the best opportunities, young people who expect varied transportation options, and businesses that seek a healthy environment for employees.

The CityHealth policy package is not an exhaustive list for solving every pressing local problem; instead, the nine selected policies meet the specific criteria of being: (1) largely under city jurisdiction; (2) backed by evidence; (3) pragmatic, including a likelihood of gaining bipartisan support; and (4) replicable, having been successfully implemented in at least one US jurisdiction. CityHealth's policy package includes the following:

- Inclusionary zoning (e.g., affordable housing)
- High-quality pre-K
- Healthy vending
- Safer alcohol sales

- Restaurant grading
- Tobacco 21
- Smoke-free indoor air
- Complete streets
- Earned sick leave

These policies improve the health and quality of life of all residents and address some of the most persistent health disparities. The package was intentionally designed to address major domains of health, including housing, education, public safety, safe and healthy food, clean air, safe streets, and economic security.

NOT ALL POLICIES ARE CREATED EQUALLY

CityHealth does not create new policy. However, based on a city's existing laws, CityHealth identifies critical elements necessary for best-quality policy (gold medal), good policy (silver medal), and passable policy (bronze medal). Cities with no policy or a policy that did not meet minimum requirements received no medal. Overall medal results are based on the combined strength and number of programs in the policy package a city has in place.

By defining gold, silver, and bronze criteria for each of the nine policies, this framework recognizes the subtle but important differences between policies that appear to tackle the same problem. Paid sick leave laws in the context of COVID-19 are a good example of these nuances. When attempting to control any infectious disease outbreak, if fewer people come to work sick because they are afforded paid time off, the rate of exposure to disease is reduced, protecting coworkers and their families and stemming the spread of illness. The United States is one of two industrialized nations without nationally guaranteed earned sick leave.[5] During the pandemic, Congress provided temporary earned sick leave requirements specifically for COVID-19, but these were set to expire on December 31, 2020. Prior to the pandemic, in the absence of a federal earned sick leave requirement, 23 of the nation's 40 largest cities by the end of 2019 provided this critical employee protection through earned sick leave policies. However, there is substantial variation among the employee protections in these cities (see Figure 6-1).[6] Of the 23 cities with an earned sick leave CityHealth medal, five received a gold medal, six received a silver medal, and 12 received a bronze medal. While the presence of earned sick leave law affords employees of that city more protection than what is provided by the federal government, provisions like allowing employees to use earned sick leave to care for family members or for domestic violence recovery, allowing employees to earn 40 or more hours, and requiring earned sick leave for all businesses regardless of size are necessary elements for the strongest policies that give employees the most comprehensive protection. Requirements for gold, silver, and bronze medals for each of the nine policies are detailed at www.cityhealth.org.

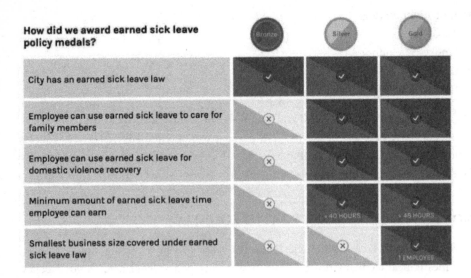

Source: Reprinted with permission from CityHealth.[6]
Figure 6-1. Medal Requirements for Earned Sick Leave

FOUR YEARS OF PROGRESS

Policymakers often turn to programs and interventions to improve the nation's health. However, these can be expensive, unsustainable, and limited in scope. Between 2017 and 2020, CityHealth contributed to significant policy uptake across the nation's 40 largest cities. In 2020, 90% (36 of 40 cities) of America's largest cities earned an overall medal, an increase from 75% in 2019 and nearly double the number from CityHealth's first assessment in 2017 (47.5%). More than 43 million people now live in a city that has earned an overall medal, compared with 29 million in 2017. Cities receiving an overall gold medal (five or more gold medals across each of the nine policies) doubled between 2017 (five cities) and 2019 (10 cities). There was a reduction in the number of cities that were unable to receive an overall medal (fewer than four gold/silver/bronze medals across the nine policies), declining from 21 cities in 2017 to four cities in 2020. In 2020, all 40 cities earned a gold medal for Tobacco 21, up from just 13 cities in 2017. This achievement was the result of locally driven innovation that eventually became federal law in December 2019.

POLICY AS A PATH TO PROMOTE EQUITY

CityHealth is making a clear and potent argument: putting local policies in place that address things like affordable housing, quality education, public safety, safe and healthy food, clean air, and economic security can have profound benefits for residents and for cities overall. CityHealth's goal is that all city leaders will use this assessment as a tool to work together and move toward the gold standard for each policy. These data are intended to serve as an accountability framework, giving residents, policymakers, and community leaders the tools to drive health improvements in their cities. Following the social justice uprisings during the summer of 2020, the need to enact policies that can bridge gaps and address disparities is of critical importance. To create communities where all residents have a chance at optimal health, policy must be used proactively as an efficient and effective tool to foster economic prosperity, health, and wellness. Until then, little progress toward reducing existing health disparities will be made.

CityHealth will again assess cities using this policy package in 2021, with plans to release an expanded policy package and assess additional cities beginning in 2022. Follow CityHealth updates at www.cityhealth.org.

REFERENCES

1. Lai KKR, Oppel Jr RA, Gebeloff R, Wright W, Smith M. The fullest look yet at the racial inequity of coronavirus. July 2020. Available at: https://www.nytimes.com/interactive/2020/07/05/us/coronavirus-latinos-african-americans-cdc-data.html. Accessed January 21, 2021.

2. Maldonado C. Mass evictions set to begin – communities of color to be hardest hit. July 2020. Available at: https://www.forbes.com/sites/camilomaldonado/2020/07/24/mass-evictions-set-to-begincommunities-of-color-to-be-hardest-hit/?fbclid=IwAR1QX0J51lyTHZpQbbfkZdcVxBMsUIdfH9sdRMULD8tmttTUf-UQVpb_zXU#127a551b4649. Accessed January 21, 2021.

3. Castrucci B, Auerbach J. Meeting individual social needs falls short of addressing social determinants of health. Health Affairs Blog. January 2019. Available at: https://www.healthaffairs.org/do/10.1377/hblog20190115.234942/full. Accessed January 21, 2021.

4. Commission on Social Determinants of Health. Closing the gap in a generation. 2008. Available at: https://www.who.int/social_determinants/final_report/csdh_finalreport_2008.pdf. Accessed December 26, 2020.

5. Raub A, Chung P, Batra P, et al. Paid leave for personal illness: a detailed look at approaches across OECD countries. World Policy Center. 2018. Available at: https://www.worldpolicycenter.org/sites/default/files/WORLD%20Report%20-%20Personal%20Medical%20Leave%20OECD%20Country%20Approaches_0.pdf. Accessed December 26, 2020.

6. CityHealth. Earned sick leave policy breakdown. 2019. Available at: https://static1.squarespace.com/static/5ad9018bf93fd4ad7295ba8f/t/5dcb72fa1c9bb248f63c7537/1573614333217/CityHealth_EarnedSick_Nov2019.pdf. Accessed December 26, 2020.

7

Using the Health Impact in Five Years (HI-5) Model

Elizabeth L. Skillen, PhD, MS and Meghan Roney, MPH

Disclaimer: The findings and conclusions in this chapter are those of the author(s) and do not necessarily represent the official position of the Centers for Disease Control and Prevention (CDC).

INTRODUCTION

Public health practitioners face increasing challenges to addressing the drivers of health and well-being.[1] For example, clinical care isn't the only thing that affects our health. Social and economic factors (40%), health behaviors (30%), and physical environment (10%) have a larger impact on health outcomes than clinical care alone (20%).[2] Conditions in the places where we live, learn, work, and play—defined as the social determinants of health (SDOH)—affect a wide range of health risks and outcomes. For example, low-income or unsafe neighborhoods, unstable housing,[3] and poor-quality education can have detrimental impacts on health.[4] Conversely, safe and affordable housing and access to education, public safety, and environments free of life-threatening toxins can promote health at the individual and population levels.[5] Taking action on these SDOH can support efforts to eliminate health disparities and achieve health equity—i.e., "the attainment of the highest level of health for all people."[6] The US Department of Health and Human Services (HHS) includes health equity as an overarching goal in its 10-year agenda—known as Healthy People 2030—for improving the nation's health.[7] HHS's Healthy People 2030 sets out a plan of action that "support(s) the implementation of evidence-based programs and policies" and provides a framework for public health practitioners to incorporate SDOH into core public health practice.[6] There is an opportunity to further population health improvement efforts nationally by enhancing public health practitioners' ability to work across health and non-health sectors to address SDOH.[1]

There is a large literature base that shows the relationship between poverty and poor health.[8,9,10] The burden of poverty and the resulting health outcomes disproportionately affect communities of color, as evidenced by data from the US Census Bureau that show higher poverty rates among Black (20.8%), Hispanic (17.6%), and Asian people (10.1%)

compared with non-Hispanic White people (8.5%).[11] Low-income families often lack access to health care, healthy food, public transportation, and adequate housing.[12] Poverty is also associated with adverse health outcomes for children, including exposure to adverse childhood experiences.[13,14,15] Earned Income Tax Credits (EITCs) help low-to-moderate-income working people keep more of the money they earn by enabling them to pay lower taxes or to get a bigger tax refund. To qualify, individuals must have earned income (e.g., wages or salary), meet basic eligibility requirements (e.g., income and investment limits), and file a tax return.[16] Research shows that the EITC is an effective policy solution to lift people out of poverty, improve health outcomes, and achieve health equity, particularly among infants and mothers.[17,18] For example, in 2018, the Internal Revenue Service processed more than 26 million returns claiming an EITC, resulting in more than $64 billion in EITCs to eligible filers.[19] States have also expanded the EITC; 29 states, the District of Columbia, and Puerto Rico currently have an EITC.[20]

To better support public health professionals and decision makers in their efforts to address SDOH, to make the healthy choice the easy choice, and to achieve health equity, the CDC developed the Health Impact in Five Years (HI-5) Initiative.[21] The HI-5 Initiative highlights 14 nonclinical, community-wide interventions (CWIs) that have evidence of positive health impacts within five years and cost-effectiveness (in some cases, cost savings) over the lifetime of the population or sooner. Through HI-5, the CDC provides credible evidence on CWIs, including policy options, to inform public health practitioners' efforts to improve population health. Yet working to address SDOH is more effective with knowledge not only of the evidence but also how to use policy as a tool to address public health concerns.[22]

To identify opportunities for public health to implement HI-5 interventions, the CDC Foundation, with technical consultation from the CDC and funding from the Robert Wood Johnson Foundation, created the HI-5 Partner Consortium (HI-5 Consortium) and launched a project to gather, synthesize, and translate existing evidence, practice-based evidence, and lessons learned on the effective implementation of two of the HI-5 CWIs: EITCs and Public Transportation Introduction and Expansion (Public Transportation). The HI-5 Consortium thought it beneficial to explore how public health practitioners could engage in non-health policy processes as part of population health improvement efforts. With the support of the HI-5 Consortium, the CDC Foundation assessed what states and local jurisdictions needed to implement select HI-5 CWIs and considered the unique role of health in enacting and implementing EITC and Public Transportation policies. For communities considering implementing these HI-5 interventions, we will describe the HI-5 menu of policy options, the rationale for policy selection, and the strategies and technical assistance that the CDC and the CDC Foundation have used to help public health practitioners and decision makers incorporate evidence into the policy process (Figure 7-1).[21]

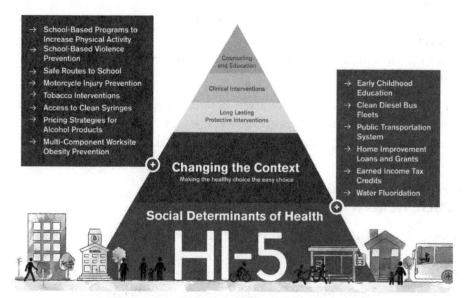

Source: Reprinted from CDC.[21]

Figure 7-1. Health Impact in 5 Years

HOW THE HI-5 LIST WAS DEVELOPED

The CDC developed the HI-5 Initiative by starting with a broad review of interventions that had strong evidence of health outcomes, rather than focusing on a set of interventions intended to address a specific set of health conditions, such as heart disease or asthma.[23] The CDC initially identified more than 250 CWIs that had the highest evidence rating from the Community Guide[24] and County Health Rankings and Roadmaps' "What Works for Health."[25] The CDC reviewed the evidence, excluded clinical interventions, and assessed more than 120 interventions against the following inclusion criteria:[26]

- Community-Wide/Population-Oriented: Focus on whole populations or whole communities.
- Measurable Impact on Health: Has evidence of a positive impact on health within five years of implementation; evidence for each health outcome must include a systematic review, at least three randomized controlled trials, or three quasi-experimental studies with comparisons or with direct evidence of impact (e.g., exposure to particulate matter).
- Available Economic Data: Has evidence reporting cost-effectiveness, and in some cases cost savings, over the lifetime of the population or sooner.

- Intervention Not at Saturation: Has not been carried out in at least 85% of communities or states.
- Broad Level of Impact: Evidence that the intervention was implemented at the policy level or at large scale in multiple settings.

Consultations occurred with subject matter experts across the CDC to identify additional CWIs supported by systematic reviews. The CDC then created HI-5 evidence briefs with health outcomes and cost data for decision makers.

POLICY DEVELOPMENT: AN ESSENTIAL PUBLIC HEALTH FUNCTION

Public health professionals have an important role in policy processes related to SDOH, including the approaches identified in HI-5.[27] They can analyze policies, share findings, build partnerships, and promote solutions supported by scientific studies. Practitioners' efforts can be enhanced with training in how to assess the complex interactions among individual, institutional, and societal factors embedded in SDOH policy processes.[28] Yet there are gaps in workforce capacity to engage in policy processes in non-health sectors. The 2017 Public Health Workforce Interests and Needs Survey is a nationally representative survey that assessed public health professionals from 47 state health agencies, 25 large-city agencies, and select local agencies in 20 critical skills, including workforce awareness of emerging concepts.[29] One such concept is the "health in all policies" strategy, which is "a collaborative approach to improving the health of all people by incorporating health considerations into decision-making across sectors and policy areas."[30] Notably, of the 60% of respondents who were aware of this "health in all policies" approach, only 50% perceived it as integral to their day-to-day work. These findings underscore the need to enhance health officials' policy fluency to build the capacity that is critical to selecting and implementing approaches like HI-5.[1] Moreover, the survey identified a gap in public health practitioners' knowledge and skills related to working across health and non-health sectors to address SDOH.

STRATEGIES FOR MULTISECTOR COLLABORATION: THE CDC AND THE CDC FOUNDATION HI-5 PARTNER CONSORTIUM

The CDC and Federal Partnership for HI-5

As a federal agency, the CDC engaged in dissemination of evidence as a first step to raise awareness and provide options, such as those included in HI-5, for decision makers. The CDC launched HI-5 in August 2016 in a national Dialogue4Health webinar with more than 1,000 participants.[31] Since then, the CDC has promoted the evidence through speaking engagements, "stories from public health innovators," publications, and technical assistance. To learn more about how states and communities are implementing HI-5 CWIs, the CDC has supported collaborations across different fields with many public health professional organizations like the Association of State and Territorial Health Officials (ASTHO), the National Association of County and City Health Officials (NACCHO), and the National Network of Public Health Institutes (NNPHI). The CDC also works with federal partners like the Department of Housing and Urban Development and the Federal Transit Administration.

Efforts to Gather Practice-Based Evidence

Not all organizations and disciplines are in the business of health, which makes engaging across sectors a complex balance of identifying ways to work together on common missions and goals.[32] For example, experts in tax policy and economic security may have a common mission with public health to "inform, educate, and empower communities," but they would expect to do so through economic policy rather than by monitoring health and identifying or diagnosing health hazards. Therefore, translating health outcomes and cost data, like those identified in HI-5, can reveal a common mission, and highlight a pathway toward working together. Identifying specific roles that public health could play related to data analysis, partnership, or messaging makes it easier to engage in cross-sector work.[33]

To better understand the policy implementation processes used by health departments, multisector partners, and decision makers, the CDC Foundation, with technical consultation from the CDC and supported by the HI-5 Partner Consortium, conducted a project focused on two HI-5 interventions, EITC and Public Transportation. The goals of the project were to gather lessons learned, practice-based evidence, and promising practices; to identify enabling conditions and policy components that lead to effective implementation; and to identify public health's role in EITC and Public Transportation policy work. To achieve these goals, the CDC Foundation used a combination of convenings and key informant interviews for both HI-5 interventions. For example, to explore the ways that public health can work on addressing income insecurity through EITCs, the CDC Foundation interviewed and convened leading state and local stakeholders (health and non-health) that already had developed, enacted, and implemented successful policies for state EITCs. In addition, to obtain feedback on a prototype EITC Action Guide, the CDC Foundation conducted a follow-up convening with stakeholders who had interest in EITCs but had not yet enacted one in their state. Throughout this process, stakeholders consisted of advocacy groups, public health professionals, and budget and policy professionals. The CDC Foundation synthesized the themes across all the key informant interviews and convenings into a final report, "Health Impact in Five Years (HI-5): Lessons from the Field on the Earned Income Tax Credit and Public Transportation."[33] The convenings and key informant interviews revealed that public health has the potential to play a key role in advancing EITC policy. The CDC Foundation learned from stakeholders the potential roles public health can play, including

- Serving as a credible voice on the value of EITCs to health outcomes and equity;
- Building the evidence that shows the health impacts of EITCs;
- Developing and coordinating coalitions; and
- Using close connections with EITC-eligible recipients to help more people take advantage of the benefit.[33]

The final report[33] depicts select state-specific contexts that influence the interactions among institutions and individuals engaging in EITC policy efforts, including success stories. For example, the General Court of the Commonwealth of Massachusetts adopted an EITC in 2015 with input from a statewide coalition of community action agencies, antipoverty agencies, and sectors including housing, education, and public health. Massachusetts recognized the need to message health and EITC together, framing EITC as a medicine that can improve health and reduce stress. Following initial success, Massachusetts expanded its EITC in 2018 (G.L. c. 62, § 6(h))..

This work also informed two tools that the CDC Foundation created to synthesize concrete actions for practitioners: the EITC Public Health Action Guide[34] and the Public Transportation Public Health Action Guide.[35] These tools describe ways public health professionals can address SDOH by engaging in these nontraditional health interventions in partnership with groups outside of public health. The guides articulate the health aspects of non-health-sector interventions, offer a simple self-assessment to help the reader reflect on how ready the community is for these interventions, and suggest some simple actions to take based on community context. The HI-5 Consortium project has identified practical actions that public health can take to address two areas of SDOH described in Healthy People 2030.

ESSENTIAL SKILLS FOR NEXT-GENERATION PUBLIC HEALTH PRACTICE

To reduce health disparities, the public health workforce of the future will require new skills, including systems thinking and coalition building, to incorporate proven health-improving solutions into non-health-sector domains.[1] Despite the availability of evidence related to the HI-5 CWIs, public health professionals and policymakers may not have ready access to or awareness of the health and economic value of these community-wide approaches, and how best to apply supporting evidence. Further, the CDC continues to build the evidence base to address SDOH.[36] The CDC Foundation heard from stakeholders about a critical need to continue to develop public health professionals and help them access tools and resources to address the social determinants.[33]

The CDC Foundation, with technical support from the CDC, and the HI-5 Partner Consortium are identifying ways in which public health professionals can address SDOH by translating evidence across sectors. This work builds awareness of how non-health-sector interventions can impact health and identifies simple things public health professionals can do. The CDC Foundation is considering other efforts to gather and disseminate information about what works in addressing SDOH and may identify new activities to build skills in the public health workforce to enhance health solutions through policy.[33]

REFERENCES

1. Department of Health and Human Services. A call to action to create a 21st century public health infrastructure. Available at: https://www.healthypeople.gov/sites/default/files/Public-Health-3.0-White-Paper.pdf#:~:text=%20%20%20Title%20%20%20Public%20Health,Created%20Date%20%20%2010%2F14%2F2016%202%3A42%3A09%20PM%20. Accessed September 2, 2020.

2. County Health Rankings and Road Maps. County health rankings model. 2014. Available at: https://www.countyhealthrankings.org/explore-health-rankings/measures-data-sources/county-health-rankings-model. Accessed September 2, 2020.

3. Pollack C, Egerter S, Sadegh-Mobari T, Dekker M, Braveman P. Where we live matters for our health: the links between housing and health. Issue brief 2: housing and health. Princeton, NJ: Robert Wood Johnson Foundation, Commission to Build a Healthier America; 2008.

4. Department of Health and Human Services. Healthy People 2030 evidence summaries. Available at: https://health.gov/healthypeople/objectives-and-data/social-determinants-health/literature-summaries. Accessed September 12, 2020.

5. National Academies of Sciences, Engineering, and Medicine. Leading health indicators 2030: advancing health, equity, and well-being. Washington, DC: The National Academies Press; 2020.

6. Liburd LC, Hall JE, Mpofu JJ, Williams SM, Bouye K, Penman-Aguilar A. Addressing health equity in public health practice: frameworks, promising strategies, and measurement considerations. *Annu Rev Public Health*. 2020;41(1):417–32.

7. Department of Health and Human Services. Healthy People 2030 framework. Available at: https://www.healthypeople.gov/2020/About-Healthy-People/Development-Healthy-People-2030/Framework. Accessed September 2, 2020.

8. Marmot M, Wilkinson R. *Social determinants of health*. Oxford, England: Oxford University Press; 2005.

9. Bosworth B, Burtless G, Zhang K. Later retirement, inequality in old age, and the growing gap in longevity between rich and poor. Washington, DC: The Brookings Institution; 2016.

10. Thornton RLJ, Glover CM, Cené CW, Glik DC, Henderson JA, Williams DR. Evaluating strategies for reducing health disparities by addressing the social determinants of health. *Health Aff (Millwood)*. 2016;35(8):1416–23.

11. Semega J, Kollar M, Creamer J, Mohanty A. Income and poverty in the United States: 2018. Report Number P60-266. US Census Bureau. September 10, 2019. Available at: https://www.census.gov/library/publications/2019/demo/p60-266.html. Accessed April 13, 2021.

12. Woolf S, Aron L, Dubay L, Simon S, Zimmerman E, Luk K. How are income and wealth linked to health and longevity? Urban Institute Center for Health Policy. 2015.

13. Strully KW, Rehkopf DH, Xuan Z. Effects of prenatal poverty on infant health: state earned income tax credits and birth weight. *Am Sociol Rev*. 2010;75(4):534–62.

14. Hair NL, Hanson JL, Wolfe BL. Association of child poverty, brain development, and academic achievement. *JAMA Pediatrics*. 2015;169(9):822–29.

15. Centers for Disease Control and Prevention (CDC). Preventing adverse childhood experiences: leveraging the best available evidence. Atlanta: National Center for Injury Prevention and Control, Centers for Disease Control and Prevention; 2019.

16. Internal Revenue Service (IRS). Earned Income Tax Credit. Available at: https://www.irs.gov/credits-deductions/individuals/earned-income-tax-credit. Accessed September 2, 2020.

17. Hoynes H, Miller D, Simon D. Income, the earned income tax credit, and infant health. *Am Econ J Econ Pol*. 2015;7(1):172–211.

18. Centers for Disease Control and Prevention (CDC). Health Impact in 5 Years. Earned income tax credits. Available at: https://www.cdc.gov/policy/hst/hi5/taxcredits/index.html. Accessed September, 2 2020.

19. Internal Revenue Service (IRS). Earned income tax credit statistics. Available at: https://www.irs.gov/credits-deductions/individuals/earned-income-tax-credit/earned-income-tax-credit-statistics. Accessed April 28, 2021.

20. Center for Budget and Policy Priorities. Policy basics: state earned income tax credits. Available at: https://www.cbpp.org/research/state-budget-and-tax/policy-basics-state-earned-income-tax-credits. Accessed April 21, 2021.

21. Centers for Disease Control and Prevention (CDC). Health Impact in 5 Years. Available at: www.cdc.gov/hi5. Accessed January 31, 2020.

22. Association of State and Territorial Health Officials, de Beaumont Foundation. Public health workforce interests and needs survey, information to action: the workforce data of Public Health WINS, summary report. 2015. Available at: https://www.astho.org/Workforce-Development-and-Research/?terms=public+health+workforce+survey. Accessed July 16, 2021.

23. Centers for Disease Control and Prevention (CDC). Health Impact in 5 Years. About the evidence summaries. Available at: https://www.cdc.gov/policy/hst/hi5/aboutsummaries/index.html. Accessed September 2, 2020.

24. The Community Guide. Available at: https://www.thecommunityguide.org. Accessed September 2, 2020.

25. The County Health Rankings and Road Maps. What works for health. Available at: https://www.countyhealthrankings.org/take-action-to-improve-health/what-works-for-health. Accessed September 2, 2020.

26. Centers for Disease Control and Prevention (CDC). Health Impact in Five Years, About the Evidence Summaries. Available at: https://www.cdc.gov/policy/hst/hi5/aboutsummaries/index.html. Accessed April 23, 2021.

27. Centers for Disease Control and Prevention (CDC). The public health system & the 10 essential public health services. Available at: https://www.cdc.gov/publichealthgateway/publichealthservices/essentialhealthservices.html. Accessed September 2, 2020.

28. Minyard K, Smith TA, Turner R, Milstein B, Solomon R. Factors influencing effective use of system dynamic models. Available at: https://onlinelibrary.wiley.com/doi/full/10.1002/sdr.1596.

29. Sellers K, Leider KJ, Gould E, et al. The state of the US governmental public health workforce, 2014–2017. *Am J Public Health*. 2019;109: 674–80.

30. Rudolph L, Caplan J, Ben-Moshe K, Dillon L. Health in all policies: a guide for state and local governments. Washington, DC, Oakland, CA: American Public Health Association and Public Health Institute; 2013.

31. Dialogue4health. HI-5: exploring community-wide interventions that have health impact in 5 years. 2016. Available at: http://www.dialogue4health.org/resource-library/detail/hi-5. Accessed September 2, 2020.

32. Roundtable on Population Health Improvement. Board on population health and public health practice. Washington, DC: National Academies Press; 2014.

33. Nicole L, McCain C. Health Impact in Five Years (HI-5): lessons from the field on the earned income tax credit and public transportation. August 2020. Available at: https://www.cdcfoundation.org/programs/HI-5. Accessed September 21, 2020.

34. CDC Foundation. EITC public health action guide. Available at: https://www.cdcfoundation.org/sites/default/files/files/PublicHealthActionGuide_EITC.pdf. Accessed September 22, 2020.

35. CDC Foundation. Public health action guide public transportation. Available at: https://www.cdcfoundation.org/sites/default/files/files/HI5_TransportationGuide.pdf. Accessed September 22, 2020.

36. Centers for Disease Control and Prevention (CDC). Social determinants of health. Available at: https://www.cdc.gov/socialdeterminants/index.htm. Accessed September 22, 2020.

8

Learning From the Promoting Health and Cost Control in States (PHACCS) Initiative: How States Can Implement Evidence-Based Policy to Address Health Inequities and Improve Population Health

Adam Lustig, MS

A person's health is impacted by where they live, their income, their educational attainment, and other factors. Differences in these factors lead to health inequities that can only be comprehensively addressed when policymakers at all levels of government make it a top priority to increase opportunities for people to be healthy and make healthy choices. This must be coupled with the removal of barriers that stand in the way of achieving better health—often a significant challenge because many of these barriers have been built into institutional practices over many decades.

It also is important to acknowledge the impact of the novel coronavirus outbreak on communities all across the country. As states responded to the crisis, they faced a new reality of balancing "business as usual" with the short- and long-term health and economic impacts of COVID-19. The outbreak continues to uncover existing disparities and the need to promote upstream prevention policies that address the social determinants of health. The new normal that states will face as the country recovers from the pandemic will require nuanced strategies to ensure that all residents' needs are being met.

State policy is an important mechanism for creating healthy environments that allow individuals and communities to thrive. This stems from state policymakers' vested interest in ensuring that their constituents can remain healthy, prosper, and reach their full potential. States are also afforded the flexibility to develop innovative solutions to the issues most important to their population. Around the country, state leaders are working to deepen knowledge of the health impacts of policies outside of the health care sector but are often met with competing demands for resources and time. As federal public health funding decreases and regulatory protections are scaled back, the role of states in promoting health and well-being is increasingly important. While local municipalities play an important role in adopting innovative approaches to addressing public health challenges, state laws can serve as a catalyst for and in some cases limit actions at the local level.

To provide state leaders with timely and relevant information, Trust for America's Health (TFAH) launched the Promoting Health and Cost Control in States (PHACCS) initiative to identify and support the adoption of evidence-based policies from around the country.[1] Since its creation in late 2017, the PHACCS initiative has provided state leaders and advocates with the actionable information needed to improve population health and control costs over time. We identified 13 evidence-based public health and prevention policies to support cross-sector collaborative opportunities, specifically focusing on their impacts in improving people's well-being and states' strategies to control costs. Our final list of recommended policies, shown in Figure 8-1, is meant to provide a menu of options for state leaders to explore as they consider how best to use their state's resources to improve their population's health and well-being.[2]

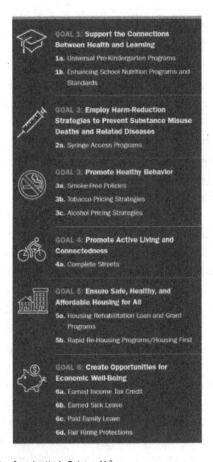

Source: Reprinted with permission from Lustig A, Cabrera M.[2]

Figure 8-1. PHACCS Goals and Recommended Policies

TFAH reviewed more than 1,500 policies from a number of nationally recognized databases and identified policies that had the following four characteristics:

1. Strength and existence of health impact and economic evidence
2. Population-based prevention effort
3. Form of primary or secondary prevention
4. Clear role for state legislative action

We often are asked if our list of 13 recommended policies is exhaustive. The short answer is no. However, in consultation with leading experts across many fields, we believe that this list represents a menu of actionable, politically feasible policies that address critical issues facing many states. Our policies address six different areas: education, harm reduction, healthy behaviors, built environment, affordable housing, and economic well-being.

EDUCATION

There is broad recognition of the critical importance of early childhood education and access to nutritious meals to the health of developing children. Many families and children continue to face enormous challenges in accessing developmentally appropriate, high-quality early care and education in safe and healthy settings. High-quality universal or state-sponsored pre-kindergarten programs not only better prepare children for the transition to kindergarten but can also have positive impacts later in life, such as academic success and lower poverty rates.

Like many adults, most children in the United States are not eating enough nutritious foods or getting enough physical activity. States can establish policies to strengthen or augment requirements related to the nutritional value of foods served in school settings and expand access to free or reduced-price school breakfast or lunch. Access to nutritious meals and snacks in schools can improve academic achievement and reduce body mass index, both of which can be linked to decreasing health care costs over time.

HARM REDUCTION

As states grapple with the opioid crisis, many of the policies being promoted address access to addiction treatment (e.g., medication-assisted therapy) or preventing overdoses (e.g., access to naloxone). While these interventions are critical in turning the tide and helping individuals addicted to opioids, we must also consider how to prevent costly blood-borne diseases that are associated with injection drug use. Syringe service programs play an important role in reducing harm among individuals who inject drugs. As one of the most tried and true strategies for reducing transmission of blood-borne diseases and significantly reducing health care costs, syringe service programs have seen an increase in attention over the past few years in states that have previously been hesitant to adopt such programs. With the annual costs of treatment for hepatitis C virus, hepatitis B virus, and human immunodeficiency virus ranging from $84,000 to $379,000 per person, preventing infection from these viruses can yield cost savings within a single year.[3]

HEALTHY BEHAVIORS

While a majority of our recommendations are not policies that a reader would typically associate with public health, we highlight a number of long-standing interventions that have not kept pace in the 21st century. Tobacco use continues to be the leading cause of preventable death in the United States and a major cost driver to the health care system (to the tune of $170 billion per year). Nevertheless, many states have been hesitant to raise their tobacco taxes and expand smoke-free policies. Decades of research has shown that higher tobacco prices decrease consumption while increasing rates of tobacco cessation. Combined with smoke-free policies, these strategies can reduce health care costs associated with poor tobacco-related health outcomes and increase revenue for states. Similar to the impact that tobacco taxes have on consumption, higher taxes on alcoholic beverages have also been shown to reduce alcohol-related harms. Despite all 50 states having some form of alcohol tax, these levies have not kept up with inflation and thus their impact has eroded over time.

BUILT ENVIRONMENT

Another area that is seeing increased attention from policymakers nationwide is the importance of community connectivity and pedestrian safety. State-level Complete Streets policies can incentivize and require local governments to consider the needs of pedestrians, bicyclists, transit riders, and motorists when making planning decisions. Complete Streets policies improve connectivity to transportation systems, promote physical activity, encourage biking and walking, and make places more pedestrian friendly. Not only do these policies increase physical activity by creating safer environments for pedestrians and non-motor vehicle users, but they can also serve as an economic driver to local businesses by increasing foot traffic.

AFFORDABLE HOUSING

Access to safe and affordable housing is an issue faced by state and local officials across the country. Most national news coverage tends to highlight the struggles of major cities, but rural jurisdictions also find it hard to identify solutions to reduce homelessness and housing insecurity. Despite housing issues often being addressed at the local level, states can enact policies, such as requiring adoption of the Housing First and Rapid Rehousing approaches, to better connect people experiencing chronic homelessness with permanent housing and supportive services. These policies have been shown to decrease rates of homelessness, decrease the length of time families and individuals remain homeless, and increase access to social services.[4] States also can address unsafe housing conditions for low- and median-income families by providing funding to Housing Rehabilitation Loan and Grant Programs. These programs focus on removing health or safety hazards (e.g., mold) and improving a home's energy efficiency. These types of home improvements have been shown to boost overall physical and mental health, in addition to having positive effects on a neighborhood's quality and stability.[5,6]

ECONOMIC WELL-BEING

There is little doubt about the linkages between poverty and poor health. Poverty is both a cause and a consequence of poor health, in turn making it a critical issue for policymakers to address in a meaningful way. Recognizing the inextricable link between health and poverty, state policymakers can use a number of policy levers to encourage employment for working individuals and families (e.g., Earned Income Tax Credit), provide meaningful benefits (e.g., Paid Family Leave and Earned Sick Leave), and make it possible for job applicants to be considered on their qualifications and not solely on their conviction history (e.g., Ban the Box). These policies can increase financial stability for low-income workers, encourage the use of preventative services, increase worker productivity, enable individuals to care for sick loved ones, and encourage reentry into the workforce for justice-involved individuals.

CONCLUSION

Despite the plethora of evidence supporting TFAH's list of policies, there are still significant opportunities for states to enact and effectively implement the PHACCS recommendations. We will continue to work with state decision-makers, advocates, and other key partners to advance these policies, but at the end of the day policymakers will need to demonstrate leadership and act decisively to truly improve our nation's health.

Acknowledgments: The author would like to thank Marilyn Cabrera, MPH, for her contributions to the PHACCS initiative.

REFERENCES

1. Trust for America's Health. Promoting Health and Cost Control in States (PHACCS). Available at: https://www.tfah.org/initiatives/promoting-health-cost-control-states-phaccs. Accessed January 24, 2020.

2. Lustig A, Cabrera M. Promoting health and cost control in states: how states can improve community health and well-being through policy change. February, 2019. Available at: https://www.tfah.org/wp-content/uploads/2019/02/2019-PHACCS-Report_FINAL.pdf. Accessed April 23, 2020.

3. Belani HK, Muennig PA. Cost-effectiveness of needle and syringe exchange for the prevention of HIV in New York City. *J HIV AIDS Soc Serv.* 2008;7(3):229–40.

4. County Health Rankings & Roadmaps. Rapid re-housing programs. Available at: https://www.countyhealthrankings.org/take-action-to-improve-health/what-works-for-health/strategies/rapid-re-housing-programs. Updated March 1, 2019. Accessed April 23, 2020.

5. County Health Rankings & Roadmaps. Housing rehabilitation loan & grant programs. Available at: http://www.countyhealthrankings.org/take-action-to-improve-health/what-works-for-health/policies/housing-rehabilitation-loan-grant-programs. Updated September 29, 2019. Accessed April 23, 2020.

6. Gibson M, Petticrew M, Bambra C, et al. Housing and health inequalities: a synthesis of systematic reviews of interventions aimed at different pathways linking housing and health. *Health Place.* 2011;17(1):175–84.

DIFFERENT TOOLS, SAME GOAL

9

Politics as a Public Health Imperative

Abdul El-Sayed, MD, DPhil

I had my work cut out for me when I became Detroit's health director in 2015. I was charged with rebuilding the city's health department, which had previously been shut down and privatized when Detroit was facing bankruptcy and a state financial take-over. Though the work was arduous, we were guided by the foundational pillars of public health.

We focused on the well-being of children, leveraging health to disrupt intergenerational poverty. That meant testing schools for lead and implementing mitigation plans. That meant providing every child who needed them a free pair of glasses and vision testing. That meant going after the Marathon petroleum refinery—the biggest polluter in the most polluted zip code in the entire state of Michigan—and forcing them to use their own money to reduce their emissions.

In my role, I could see the upper limits of what could be achieved within the bureaucracy of public health. I realized that so much of what we could accomplish was conditioned on what politicians wanted. As the Flint water crisis unfolded, I watched as the same system of emergency management that had shut down our health department was now poisoning Flint, a postindustrial city much like Detroit, with a largely low-income and Black population. Then I watched an individual with no care for the public welfare—or frankly anyone other than himself or those he felt could help him—get elected president.

That was when I asked myself about my obligation to the moment.

I channeled my belief in the vital role of public health to our public welfare and the critical need for more engaged policy leadership into a run for the governor of Michigan. My campaign platform centered on universal health care access for every Michigander and a strong public health infrastructure. We also operationalized the social determinants of health into policies focusing on universal broadband, free access to water (in a state with more fresh water than any other place on Earth), and equitable education funding. As a child of Egyptian immigrants raised by my immigrant father and my Daughter-of-the-American-Revolution stepmother and as a Muslim-American, I knew my story could help remind us who we are at the core: a society that prides itself on the notion of *e pluribus unum*—out of many, one.

Although I did not win my race, we built an impressive infrastructure on which to move these goals forward. We created the Southpaw Michigan political action committee to continue driving our vision of a more just, equitable, and sustainable state. We work with each of our endorsed candidates—progressive champions we help get elected—to ensure a commitment to the central tenets of public health, equity, collective action, and judging policies by how they help or hurt Michiganders, not simply a bottom line.

As I hope my story demonstrates, public health professionals, advocates, and allies are key to building a politics that values public health. We need to leverage our voices and our votes in the fight for public health.

Politics is simply the system by which we allocate scarce resources. In a world where some people get to be healthy and others don't, health is a scarce resource, too. And that means public health is inherently political. Unless we're willing to embrace that and do the work of politicking for public health, we will consistently miss one of our most important opportunities to shape the health and well-being of our communities. What's worse, the enemies of public health—the corporations that have long opposed our policies and the politicians who willingly accept their money to do their bidding—are out there, too. If we choose not to take up the mantle of politics, we must know that we are leaving their influences unchecked. We don't have a choice. It is public health malpractice to ignore the politics happening around us, and we have a responsibility to act when we see those politics making people sick.

We can start by rethinking our place in politics. We've been fooled by the misconception that because public health is led by science it is somehow a sterile enterprise, and therefore that what we do is apolitical. That couldn't be further from the truth. Science, and in effect public health, is absolutely political—especially in a moment when people are trying to advocate for a politics that denies and debases science.

Political activity takes many forms. For one, supporting voter registration and voter turnout is a public health necessity. In a democracy, your vote is your agency, and any loss of agency harms our collective health. All of us should strive to achieve the broadest possible suffrage in our country, helping register people to vote and making sure they get out to the polls on Election Day. It also means supporting policies like no-reason absentee voting, vote-by-mail, and making Election Day a national holiday.

Second, as "public health people" we often take for granted how important public health is, and we assume that others automatically agree. So we often miss opportunities to advocate for it on the agendas of people with power. Public health advocates need to be involved in political campaigns, both to educate candidates about policies that are in the best interest of public health and to help them get the message out to constituents. It's our job to speak up about the policies that will help people and about the policies that will hurt people.

Third, we can communicate our public health priorities by tapping into our roles as storytellers. As scientists, we are trained to value evidence-based reasoning. We use cold, hard facts to make our case. And though this is always how public policy decisions should be made, it's not necessarily how they should be communicated. Telling a good story is far more powerful than simply showing somebody the results of a study—especially when folks sometimes lack the tools to interpret those studies. Scientific research drives public health practice; it should steer us in the direction we need to go. But you've got to find the emotional motor behind the data that inspires people to act.

Many public health employees work for government agencies, which puts certain restrictions on what you can say or do. But no matter where you work, it's critical to be aware of what's happening beyond your institution. We need to understand the political landscape in which actors are making decisions. What are the larger conversations surrounding them? What does the media situation look like? And how can one, as a public health practitioner, leverage that knowledge to help the community and people in positions of power understand what's at stake?

Finally, I encourage my fellow public health colleagues to run for office. One of my greatest public health heroes is Dr. Rudolf Virchow. Known as the founding father of modern pathology, Virchow became a leader of the German Progress Party in the late 1800s. He saw the connections among health, health care, and politics, and he understood that if we fail to advance our values at the very top of the governmental system even as we work to influence the grassroots, the idea that the government is going to engage with policies that commit to those values is unfounded.

Each of us goes into this work because we believe in the responsibility and opportunity to empower people to live their best, healthiest lives. It is the role of government to promote the general welfare of the population. And insofar as our elected officials aren't doing that, we have to make sure that we are identifying that responsibility in ourselves and in the people around us. Remember, it's not that the system doesn't work—it's that the system is worked by the people who are working it. We need to be those people.

10

The Power of Regulatory Policy

Joshua M. Sharfstein, MD

Passing a new law is a great way to establish a policy that improves health. But it is far from the only way. Other important sources of policy are regulatory agencies, including state and local health departments, as well as the US Food and Drug Administration (FDA), the Environmental Protection Agency, the Consumer Product Safety Commission, the Center for Medicare & Medicaid Services, and the US Department of Agriculture. These agencies operate under statutes that provide some latitude to determine how best to advance critical public goals, such as a safe environment, a safe food supply, and a market of safe and effective medical products.

These laws give agencies a variety of mechanisms for action, including

- Regulations: Agencies propose, take public comment on, and then finalize regulations that have the effect of law. For example, under the Clean Air Act, the Environmental Protection Agency during the Obama Administration put in place limitations on carbon emissions of power plants. The goal was to reduce the electric industry's carbon output by about one-third.
- Regulatory guidance: Agencies can issue nonbinding guidance to encourage behaviors by regulated parties, such as the pharmaceutical industry. The FDA issues several guidances each month to help drug companies do everything from design trials for drugs to counter smallpox to create new preparations of corticosteroids for hemorrhoids.
- Regulatory judgments: Many regulatory agencies have processes for granting approvals and licenses—as well as processes for revoking them. For example, state health departments license addiction treatment centers, an activity that gives them substantial authority to promote their quality. Every local restaurant inspection is a regulatory judgment as well.
- Enforcement: Agencies can threaten or take enforcement action against individuals and businesses for violating the law. Because penalties can include fines and even jail time, even the threat of agency action can force change. For example, in 2010, a warning letter from the FDA led manufacturers of caffeinated alcoholic beverages to pull them from the market. In 2012, Baltimore City stopped the sale of contaminated children's jewelry to protect against lead poisoning.

ADVANTAGES AND DISADVANTAGES

There are advantages and disadvantages to pursuing policy change through regulatory agencies. The first advantage is that new legislation, which can be challenging to pass under the best of circumstances, is not required for regulatory action. Public health officials can strengthen oversight of the drug and device industry; medical practices; oil, gas, and chemical companies; and other major industries without needing to assemble a legislative coalition to develop and pass a proposal.

A second advantage is that regulatory agencies are generally required to make decisions based on evidence—a requirement that does not apply to the legislative branch of the government. As a result, public health advocates often have a better chance of convincing an agency to change direction than of persuading legislators to pass a new law that is opposed by entrenched interests.

A third advantage is that regulatory agencies are required to be responsive to the general public. Any citizen can participate in comment periods, hearings, and other opportunities for input. In some cases, such as with the FDA, the agency is required to provide a written response to all those who file petitions for action. In 2015, for example, a group of state and local health officials petitioned the FDA to add a black box warning on the labels of all benzodiazepines and opioids warning of fatal respiratory arrest when these are used in combination.[1] The agency granted the petition, affecting the labels of more than 200 products.[2]

There are a number of disadvantages, as well. In some cases, the underlying statute is not strong enough to support reasonable and prompt regulatory action. For example, the Consumer Product Safety Act sets such a high standard for the Consumer Product Safety Commission to ban products that even well-recognized dangers like crib bumpers remained on the market for many years.[3] Similarly, for many years until it was amended, the statute governing over-the-counter medications made action by the FDA on these products exceedingly time-consuming and difficult.[4]

A second problem is known as regulatory capture—when the agency orients itself to the needs of regulated parties. One component of regulatory capture is a revolving door of employment, whereby regulators take action in favor of a regulated party in return for the promise of a well-paid position with the industry after leaving government service. Reports that some FDA reviewers have joined the companies that make the very products they approved have undermined confidence in the agency. Not all examples of regulatory capture are so dry. After the Gulf Coast oil spill, reports surfaced that regulators in the US Department of the Interior were having sex and using drugs with officials in the oil and gas industry.

Even when the agency itself is making decisions based on science, more senior administration officials can be influenced by political considerations and intervene to stop regulatory action. For example, in December 2011, the Secretary of Health and

Human Services overruled the decision by expert reviewers and the FDA Commissioner to permit over-the-counter sale of emergency contraception.[5]

A third disadvantage is that courts can prevent agencies from moving forward on the grounds of either process or substance. A lawsuit on process generally asserts that the agency did not follow its established procedures or failed to abide by general administrative procedures set out in the Administrative Procedures Act. A lawsuit on substance claims that the agency never had the power to take an action in the first place. For example, the first time the FDA attempted to regulate tobacco products, the Supreme Court, by a 5–4 decision, concluded that the agency was not permitted to do so under the agency's guiding law, the Food, Drug, and Cosmetic Act.

LIVE BY THE SWORD, DIE BY THE SWORD

Regulatory actions that are easier to establish than new laws are also easier to reverse when elected leaders change. For example, soon after taking office, the Trump Administration began seeking to reverse a multitude of Obama-era environmental regulations, including the regulation to limit carbon emissions of power plants.

The challenge—and promise—of regulatory action can be seen in the recent crisis of rising youth use of e-cigarettes. Congress has yet to pass a specific law addressing these risks, while the FDA has struggled to implement restrictions.

The story begins in 2008, when e-cigarettes first entered the market. The FDA attempted to regulate them as drug-device combinations under the Food, Drug, and Cosmetic Act. This approach would have given flexibility to the agency to design a regulatory policy to maximize the benefits of these products for adult smokers while minimizing the risks to youth. However, manufacturers quickly sued, and both the district and appeals court found that the FDA could not move forward under this law. In 2010, the court instructed the FDA to use its authority under a recently passed tobacco law.

However, this law required three years of study and findings before the FDA could act. During this time, e-cigarettes grew in popularity, and manufacturers began to lobby Congress and the White House. The FDA took modest steps to reduce sales to minors, but when the FDA was ready to move forward with more substantive action, the White House slowed down and ultimately stopped the agency from doing so.

After a crisis of pulmonary injuries refocused public attention on e-cigarettes, the FDA was able to move forward to ban a wide range of flavors in certain types of products (but not others). Today the FDA retains authority under the law to set standards for e-cigarettes and take those failing to meet those standards off the market. But the story is far from over.

The electronic cigarette issue exemplifies the contradiction at the heart of regulatory power: enormous potential, with limitations both formal and informal. To maximize the chance of success, health officials should keep several final points in mind.

First, health officials at all levels should become familiar with their regulatory authority. Local health departments often conduct restaurant and other environmental inspections, which may be opportunities to introduce new standards that support public health goals. State health departments often review health care facilities, including ambulatory surgery centers, addiction treatment programs, hospitals, and long-term care facilities. Innovative approaches to regulation can better align the health care mission with health outcomes. Federal officials may have enormous regulatory responsibilities, providing major opportunities to move entire industries to better protect and promote the health of the public.

Second, no matter the scale, a regulatory process should aim to change minds as well as change policy. Even where an agency has formal authority to make a change, failing to attend to public perception can lead to a rapid reversal later. Agency statements, comment periods, and proposals are all opportunities to explain the public health purpose of actions and build a base of support for implementation and sustainability.

Third, there is no substitute for a great lawyer (or team of lawyers). Expert legal advice on both process and substance can help agencies navigate the obstacles that can slow down or stop promising initiatives.

Fourth, agencies can win by losing. If public health officials have made a strong case for protecting the public, unexpected court decisions that stop the agency can provoke a public outcry. The result can be pressure for new laws to resolve the standoff. This dynamic should encourage public officials not to be afraid of taking a reasonable legal risk to achieve a major health benefit.

Few would mistake the process of taking a regulatory action for the excitement of passing new legislation. Yet each year, while few new bills are passed into law, hundreds of health agencies of all shapes and sizes take thousands of small steps through regulation, guidance, and enforcement actions. Viewed from the perspective of this enormous impact, regulatory policy can be as rewarding for those who pursue it as it is beneficial to their communities.

REFERENCES

1. Dennis B. Health officials push FDA to add 'black box' warnings about using opioids, benzodiazepines together. *Washington Post.* February 22, 2016. Available at: https://www.washingtonpost.com/news/to-your-health/wp/2016/02/22/health-officials-push-fda-to-add-black-box-warnings-about-using-opioids-benzodiazepines-together/. Accessed April 11, 2020.

2. US Food and Drug Administration. FDA requires strong warnings for opioid analgesics, prescription opioid cough products, and benzodiazepine labeling related to serious risks and death from combined use. August 31, 2016. Available at: https://www.fda.gov/news-events/press-announcements/fda-requires-strong-warnings-opioid-analgesics-prescription-opioid-cough-products-and-benzodiazepine. Accessed April 11, 2020.

3. Frankel T. Dozens of infant deaths have been tied to a popular baby product. But regulators are too paralyzed to act. *Washington Post*. November 23, 2019. Available at: https://www.washingtonpost.com/business/economy/dozens-of-infant-deaths-have-been-tied-to-a-popular-baby-product-but-regulators-are-too-paralyzed-to-act/2019/11/23/c6348d68-f5a1-11e9-a285-882a8e386a96_story.html. Accessed April 11, 2020.

4. Sharfstein J. The unnecessary risk with over-the-counter drugs. *Politico*. July 24, 2017. Available at: https://www.politico.com/agenda/story/2017/07/24/risk-over-the-counter-drugs-fda-000482/. Accessed April 11, 2020.

5. Harris G. Plan to widen availability of morning after pill is rejected. *New York Times*. December 7, 2011. Available at: https://www.nytimes.com/2011/12/08/health/policy/sebelius-overrules-fda-on-freer-sale-of-emergency-contraceptives.html. Accessed April 11, 2020.

The Power of Litigation

Kendall Stagg, JD, Derek Carr, JD, and Todd Fraley, JD

Disclaimer: The views expressed in this chapter are those of the authors and do not necessarily represent those of any individuals or organizations with whom the authors are affiliated.

Public health and the law are essential partners. In many cases, efforts to protect public health and shape public policy through law focus on federal, state, and local legislatures and executives. However, the third branch of government—the judiciary—also plays an important role in advancing and, at times, impeding public health and equity. Although litigation cannot substitute for strong legislative and regulatory policy, it is a powerful tool for holding industry and government accountable, and for protecting the rights of politically disempowered communities. Litigation is likely to take on an increasingly prominent role as public health moves toward addressing the social, structural, and political factors that affect people's health, such as structural discrimination, income inequality, and disparities in political power.

Public health litigation can address a broad range of issues, including such traditional public health subjects as tobacco control, drug policy, consumer protection, and disputes over authority among different levels of government. But public health's reach is also expanding, particularly with the adoption of a "health in all policies" approach and a growing emphasis on upstream social and structural determinants of health. Politically charged, "new" public health issues such as labor standards, violence disruption, environmental justice, immigration policy, and climate mitigation, among others, have already resulted in high-profile litigation during the past decade and will likely remain controversial in the decades to come. Likewise, public health's refocusing in the wake of COVID-19 has put a contemporary spin on a number of classic public health legal issues, including government authority to quarantine, impose restrictions on interstate travel, and mandate vaccination for access to public services such as education. Indeed, the US Supreme Court's 1905 decision in *Jacobson v. Massachusetts*, a case regarding compulsory vaccination, is often cited as the origin of public health litigation in the United States.

Litigation is most often used to resolve discrete disputes whose outcomes directly impact only the individuals involved in the lawsuit. Yet high-impact public health litigation has the potential to affect entire communities by bringing about broad structural changes in public policy or by incentivizing precautionary measures through the threat

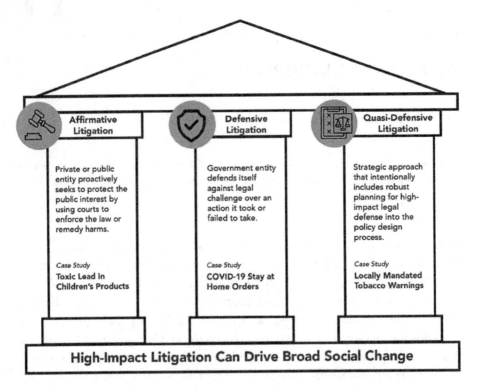

Figure 11-1. Case Studies Illustrate Three Types of High-Impact Public Health Litigation

of monetary damages (e.g., product liability cases).[1,2] As illustrated by case studies in this chapter, high-impact public health litigation takes several forms, including affirmative litigation, defensive litigation, and a strategic hybrid where public health stakeholders engage as defendants in a case they have been affirmatively planning for, much in the same manner they would plan and prepare for affirmative litigation (Figure 11-1).

Public health experts also play an indirect role in litigation by, for example, providing technical assistance and filing briefs as *amicus curiae* (literally, "a friend of the court") to help courts and the broader public understand the public health and equity implications of a particular case.

AFFIRMATIVE LITIGATION

Affirmative litigation occurs when a governmental entity or nongovernmental organization proactively seeks to protect the public interest by using courts to enforce the law or otherwise remedy harms. For example, governments have employed litigation to hold tobacco and prescription opioid manufacturers accountable for health harms resulting from their misconduct.[1-3] High-impact affirmative litigation has also long played a critical role in advancing civil rights.

Affirmative Litigation in Action

Air pollution: In Paramount, California, attorneys represented residents who lived close to a group of metal-finishing plants that were releasing cancer-causing hexavalent chromium into surrounding neighborhoods. The affirmative litigation forced plants to be temporarily shuttered until permanent changes were made to considerably lower emissions. In addition, the lawsuit generated funds to purchase air filters for 45 families living close to the facilities.

Toxic lead in children's products: As recently as 2010, lead was frequently found in toys and other products used by children. This can cause lead poisoning in children, with lifelong damage to their brains and nervous systems. A strategic combination of affirmative litigation and legislative advocacy has resulted in lead contamination becoming rare. Public health advocacy organizations still monitor this problem and file affirmative litigation when necessary. For example, the Center for Environmental Health took affirmative legal action after finding a well-known national brand selling a popular child's shoe that contained levels of lead almost 50 times over the federal lead-containment standard. They have also used affirmative litigation to mandate the removal of lead from mouthpieces of trumpets and other musical instruments played by children.

Opioids: Litigation against prescription opioid manufacturers dates back to 2001, when West Virginia sued Purdue Pharma for its alleged illegal marketing of OxyContin.[3] Since 2014—when the City of Chicago and two California counties first initiated litigation against companies involved in the manufacture, distribution, and sale of prescription opioids—thousands of cities, counties, and states have filed lawsuits against pharmaceutical companies.[2,3] These lawsuits seek compensation for the social, health, and economic costs incurred by governments in the wake of the overdose crisis and to reform industry practices that contributed to the over-prescription of opioid analgesics.[2,3] In addition to lawsuits against pharmaceutical companies, public health–related litigation has sought to publicize industry and government data related to the overdose crisis, require the provision of evidence-based, substance use disorder treatment for people in criminal justice settings, and ensure access to more affordable generic formulations of medications for treating opioid use disorder.

Tobacco: Between 1994 and 1998, 43 states and numerous local governments sued the tobacco industry for misleading the public about the harms of smoking cigarettes and sought to recover costs incurred in treating tobacco-related disease.[1-4] The litigation culminated in the Master Settlement Agreement. In addition to the financial settlement, the agreement also established a national foundation and advertising campaign to reduce tobacco-related disease and youth tobacco use, required the public release of internal industry documents, imposed restrictions on tobacco companies' marketing practices, and disbanded industry research entities and front groups.[1-4] More recently, numerous lawsuits have accused e-cigarette companies of targeting youth and misleading the public about their products, and public health organizations successfully sued the Food and Drug Administration over the agency's failure to implement and enforce federal tobacco laws.

Juul: The Center for Environmental Health brought multiple claims against Pax Labs, the original maker of Juul e-cigarettes (Juul, the world's largest e-cigarette manufacturer, was spun out of Pax Labs). The litigation ended when the parties voluntarily agreed to a court-supervised settlement, known as a consent agreement, in which no party admits liability. However, Juul did not comply with several of the agreement's requirements. As a result, the Center for Environmental Health took Juul back to court and ultimately reached a legally binding settlement with restrictions to Juul's marketing and advertising practices. The settlement marked the first time Juul agreed to legally binding restrictions on youth marketing. This affirmative litigation also resulted in Juul paying $5.5 million to fund anti-vaping advertising and prevention campaigns. The high visibility of the youth vaping epidemic made Juul a popular litigation target. By 2020, just five years after Juul hit the market, the company had already been sued by more than 100 school districts and state and local governments over its marketing practices.

Drinking water: Wheel weights made of lead are commonly used to balance tires. These weights regularly fall from vehicles and end up in storm drains, streams, and reservoirs, causing water pollution. Affirmative litigation was used to haul the largest makers of lead wheel weights into court. Prior to the lawsuit, leaded wheel weights were responsible for the release of 500,000 pounds of lead into the environment each year. Litigation and subsequent California legislation ended the use of lead wheel weights statewide. Many public health and legal experts see this important public health win as a first step toward moving the industry away from leaded wheel weights and a broader ban on the products in the United States. Similarly, residents and advocacy groups in Flint, Michigan, turned to civil litigation against government officials to redress the city's lead-contaminated water supply and the public health harms that resulted from such contamination.

DEFENSIVE LITIGATION

Defensive litigation occurs when a government entity defends itself against a legal challenge to some action it took or failed to take, such as enacting a new law or declining to issue a requested permit.[1] If asked to imagine civil litigation involving government actors, most people would likely describe defensive litigation. People default to thinking about defensive litigation for good reason—governments routinely must defend themselves against industry-backed legal challenges to laws related to tobacco, nutrition, housing, environmental standards, and economic protections, among others.

Defensive Litigation in Action

COVID-19: As state and local governments took action to protect public health by containing the spread of COVID-19, they faced lawsuits challenging so-called stay-at-home or shelter-in-place orders. These lawsuits, filed by individuals, businesses, religious institutions, and, in some cases, other governmental actors, involved claims ranging from religious discrimination to separation of powers, free speech, and due process. Lawsuits have also challenged state and local policies intended to mitigate the social and economic effects of COVID-19, such as eviction moratoriums. Additionally, widespread litigation is likely to occur if either states or the federal government mandate vaccination for COVID-19.

Plain package laws for tobacco products and smoking bans: In 2012, Australia became the first country in the world to implement a plain package law for tobacco products. For years, tobacco companies have attempted to thwart diffusion of this life-saving public health measure through intimidating lawsuits. Tobacco industry litigation to deter local and state public health ordinances is not new. Public health leaders have been defending smoking bans and youth access laws through defensive litigation for decades.

In June 2020, the World Trade Organization upheld Australia's law requiring plain tobacco packaging. This resounding victory for public health created an important legal precedent that will help protect the plain packaging laws passed by 15 other countries and paves the way for action in 12 other countries that were actively considering a plain packaging law at the time.

However, this victory in Australia does not do much (if anything) to advance tobacco control policy in the United States. As discussed in the pages that follow, plain packaging laws, advertising restrictions, and mandatory warnings all present substantial litigation risks because of First Amendment considerations unique to the United States. These types of policies should never be pursued without the assistance of public health lawyers or constitutional scholars who are knowledgeable of rapidly changing First Amendment jurisprudence.

Reproductive health: Some state and local governments have adopted regulations to limit access to contraceptive care and to ban abortions, despite evidence of how such regulations harm public health and exacerbate health inequities. Since the Supreme Court's 1973 landmark decision in *Roe v. Wade*, these regulations are routinely subject to legal challenges, with government entities engaged in defensive litigation to uphold significant restrictions on reproductive health services. For example, in 2020, the US Supreme Court struck down a Louisiana state law that required any doctor performing an abortion to have admitting privileges at a nearby hospital—a law that would have left Louisiana with only one abortion clinic statewide. In this case, the Louisiana Department of Health was engaged in defensive litigation. In contrast, three community health centers and two plaintiff doctors were engaged in affirmative litigation. This example illustrates that a single case can fall under multiple categories at the same time. Whether such litigation is defensive or affirmative depends on the vantage from which a person views the case. Moreover, depending on the underlying issue, defensive litigation can either advance or impede public health and health equity.

A STRATEGIC HYBRID: QUASI-DEFENSIVE LITIGATION

A strategic hybrid form of litigation occurs when a jurisdiction seeks to draw attention to an issue and positively influence legal doctrine by carefully designing, and subsequently adopting, a policy it knows will likely draw legal challenges. By planning for litigation in the earliest stages of the policy design process, it is possible to weave elements of affirmative, high-impact litigation strategies into what is ultimately a defensive litigation posture. More specifically, policy entrepreneurs develop an innovative policy knowing from the outset that its passage will likely spark a lawsuit. At the core of the policy development process is an awareness that a significant legal risk exists. Public health lawyers should be part of the team driving the policy design process. They can support the policy development process with substantive legal analysis and policy design decisions that maximize the potential public health benefits while also maximizing the chances the law will survive impending threats of litigation.

If a pioneering public health policy is successfully defended in court, it often creates good case law and can provide a blueprint for other jurisdictions to follow and rapidly accelerate the speed of policy diffusion. With the winds of good case law behind them, public health stakeholders can incrementally push to advance their cause even further without jeopardizing their previous legal victories. For policies that present substantial litigation risks, this strategic approach—which marries the policy development process with robust planning for legal defense—can be essential to avoiding the bad case law that often occurs with policy innovations. If successful, it is also the sweet spot that has the potential to catalyze significant policy innovation and rapid policy diffusion.

Quasi-Defensive Litigation in Action

Locally mandated tobacco health warnings: Over the last two decades, tobacco advertising has moved almost entirely to the point of sale. Many studies have found that exposure to tobacco advertising and promotion, particularly at the point of sale, is associated with increased smoking initiation, weakened resolve not to smoke, impulse purchases, brand preference, and increased difficulty quitting. In Chicago, tobacco control advocates and legislative champions wanted to mitigate the negative effects of youth exposure to tobacco advertising. However, policies combating that advertising often draw First Amendment challenges from tobacco manufacturers, retailers, and trade associations.

Specifically, the First Amendment to the US Constitution limits the government's ability to regulate speech. This limitation also affects "compelled speech," that is the government's ability to *require* people and corporations or businesses to speak. Requiring an industry to put a safety warning on products or post a warning on business premises constitutes compelled commercial speech, which is subject to a certain amount of First Amendment protection. In the context of traditional health and safety warnings, First Amendment law requires that (1) the text of the warning be "factual" and "uncontroversial," and (2) the warning requirement not be "unduly burdensome" or "unjustified." Recent court decisions must be examined to find clues as to the meaning of *factual* and *uncontroversial*, as well as what is considered *unduly burdensome* or *unjustified*.

This is exactly what the City of Chicago Department of Public Health did, with the support of public health lawyers working in the Department of Public Health, ChangeLab Solutions, and Respiratory Health Association, as well as lawyers from City Hall. Extensive legal analysis was conducted in the earliest phases of the policy design process to avoid potential First Amendment pitfalls and other legal barriers associated with the Federal Cigarette Labeling and Advertising Act (Figure 11-2).[5]

More than a year after implementing the pioneering ordinance, Chicago's locally mandated tobacco health warnings have not been challenged in court, which is likely a testament to careful and strategic legislative drafting that planned for litigation at the earliest phases of policy development. As a result of this strategic approach, QuitLine referrals are now at the point of sale throughout the city, providing an important counter-message to pervasive, point-of-sale tobacco advertising.

WARNING

CIGARS, CIGARILLOS AND MOST VAPE JUICE HAVE NICOTINE, THE SAME HIGHLY ADDICTIVE CHEMICAL IN CIGARETTES.

Want to quit? Free help available at 1-866-784-8937.

Source: Reprinted from City of Chicago.[6]

Figure 11-2. City of Chicago Warning Sign for Other Tobacco Products

Warnings on sugary drinks: As evidence increasingly links sugary drink consumption with poor health outcomes, the City and County of San Francisco enacted an ordinance that would require certain sugary drink advertisements to include a health warning. Knowing that policies requiring warning labels cannot conflict with, or include anything required by, the federal Nutrition Labeling and Education Act, public health lawyers carefully drafted their policy to avoid First Amendment claims and federal pre-emption challenges.* Unfortunately, extensive litigation has held up implementation of the law, and there is no definitive ruling on what constitutes a legally defensible warning on sugary drinks. ChangeLab Solutions has published multiple technical assistance documents on this issue, and any attempt to craft such a policy should involve public health lawyers who are well versed in these issues long before a bill or ordinance is introduced. Whether it is a warning label on sugary drinks or mandating disclosures on menus and packaging, thoughtful legal analysis and strategic planning are needed in the policy design process to improve the chances of winning in court.

Restricting the sale of menthol cigarettes: The Family Smoking Prevention and Tobacco Control Act of 2009 prohibited the sale of most flavored cigarettes, which are proven to be a starter product for kids. Unfortunately, the flavor ban did not extend to menthol-flavored cigarettes.

Mint and menthol cigarettes have unique health harms. Menthol masks the harsh taste of tobacco and entices youthful experimentation to persist long enough to become a potentially deadly addiction. The FDA has concluded that menthol cigarettes are more addictive and harder to quit. In addition, menthol-flavored cigarettes are aggressively target marketed to youth, people of color, and the LGBTQ community. For example, research has shown the industry discounts the price of menthol cigarettes near schools where Black children attend. As a result, menthol cigarettes are used at disproportionately higher rates by teens, people of color, and persons who identify as LGBTQ. Moreover, the Chicago Department of Public Health mapped retailers who sold menthol cigarettes and found they were ubiquitous near schools and in low-income neighborhoods. In response, in December 2013, Chicago passed its so-called "Buffer Zone" ordinance banning the sale of all flavored tobacco products, including menthol-flavored cigarettes, within 500 feet of schools. It was the first time any level of government—federal, state, or local—included menthol in flavored tobacco regulations.

In the policy design process, the choice to create buffer zones (rather than enact a comprehensive ban) was as much a strategic decision to best position the City of Chicago for high-risk legal defense as it was about shoring up the public acceptance, political will, and votes necessary for passage. Moreover, relying on favorable legal precedents

---

*The legal term preemption may be little known outside of courts and legislative chambers. Preemption is a legal doctrine that allows a higher level of government to limit or eliminate the power of a lower level of government to regulate a certain issue. When misused, state preemption can threaten the ability of local communities to adopt health- and equity-promoting laws and policies. Chapter 12 discusses preemption in more detail.

established in Rhode Island and New York, the definition of "flavored tobacco products" was carefully designed to avoid federal preemption pitfalls.

The City of Chicago was rapidly hit with multiple lawsuits, which it had planned for from day one. Ultimately, the City of Chicago's first-of-its kind menthol regulation was upheld and resulted in the first case law ever to address whether cities can regulate or ban the sale of menthol-flavored cigarettes. That important legal precedent has been cited as other jurisdictions seek to replicate, strengthen, and scale up restrictions on the sale of menthol cigarettes. Indeed, policy diffusion has occurred rapidly. In August 2020, Chicago's case law on menthol cigarettes was cited in a trial court opinion upholding the County of Los Angeles's complete ban on the sale of all flavored tobacco. At that time, dozens of localities had enacted complete bans on the sale of menthol cigarettes, and many others had enacted laws that restrict the sale of menthol cigarettes.

INTER-GOVERNMENTAL LITIGATION

Over the past decade, litigation on issues of public health import have increasingly involved disputes between different levels of government. The most well-known examples of inter-governmental lawsuits involve disputes between states and the federal government, such as challenges to the Affordable Care Act, immigration policies like sanctuary cities and the Deferred Action for Childhood Arrivals (DACA) program, and the rollback of environmental regulations.

A recent proliferation of state preemption laws restricting local regulatory authority has also resulted in litigation between local and state governments with respect to a wide range of equitable health policies, including paid sick leave, affordable housing and inclusionary zoning, alcohol sales control, healthy food procurement, broader food and nutrition policies, smoke-free indoor air, e-cigarette regulations, tobacco sales restrictions, and the regulation of ride sharing—to name just a few.[7]

Inter-Governmental Litigation in Action

Restoring local control in support of a trans fat ban: In 2011, the city of Cleveland, Ohio, adopted an ordinance prohibiting local grocery stores and restaurants from selling foods containing artificial trans fat. The state subsequently adopted legislation preempting Cleveland's ability to regulate food ingredients, thereby invalidating the city's trans fat ban. The city responded by suing the state, arguing that the preemptive state legislation violated Cleveland's regulatory authority. The court agreed with Cleveland, finding that the state legislature's attempt to preempt the ordinance violated the state constitution, thereby protecting the city's ability to serve as a "laboratory of democracy" for innovative public health policies.

State preemption of Birmingham's minimum wage: Birmingham, Alabama—where Black people constitute nearly 75 percent of the population—enacted a minimum wage ordinance to address economic inequities. The state legislature immediately invalidated the ordinance and prohibited localities across the state from regulating employee wages, benefits, and work schedules. Not a single Black state legislator supported the preemptive state legislation, and many viewed it as another example of Alabama lawmakers manipulating state political and legal processes to disenfranchise Black communities. Minimum-wage fast food workers, several Black lawmakers, and civil rights groups filed an equal protection lawsuit. Among other things, they argued the state law "perpetuates Alabama's *de jure* policy of white supremacy, in particular its suppression of local Black majorities through imposition of White control by state government." In December 2019, the 11th Circuit Court of Appeals sided with the State of Alabama on procedural grounds, without addressing the merits of the case.

OPPORTUNITIES AND CHALLENGES FOR PUBLIC HEALTH LITIGATION

As with all tools to protect public health and shape public policy through law, litigation presents unique opportunities and challenges. Public health litigation has been most useful and impactful in uncovering questionable industry practices and promoting transparency in government.[3,4]

Internal tobacco industry documents released as a result of government litigation against tobacco manufacturers helped improve tobacco control policy.[2,3,4] Litigation related to prescription opioids and climate change, among other crises, has also resulted in the release of otherwise confidential information related to industry misconduct, the influence of special interests on public policy, and regulatory failures.

Public health litigation can also generate revenue to support government and community-based services and to compensate those harmed by the subject of the litigation.[1-4] For example, the tobacco Master Settlement Agreement, in which tobacco manufacturers agreed to pay $206 billion over 25 years and up to $9 billion annually in perpetuity thereafter, provided hundreds of billions of dollars to state and local governments.[3] This revenue has supported critical public health efforts, despite valid criticisms of governments diverting funds obtained through the litigation for purposes wholly unrelated to public health.[3]

Revenue generated through litigation is particularly effective when used to support independent foundations dedicated to addressing public health issues. The Truth Initiative, which has overseen one of the most successful public health advertising and social-norm change campaigns in recent history, was originally established and funded by the tobacco Master Settlement Agreement.[2,3]

Additional benefits of public health litigation include deterring future misconduct, increasing public knowledge, and building political will to address public health

priorities.[1-4] Litigation settlements can also secure remedies that might have been difficult or impossible to achieve via legislative or administrative action alone, such as advertising and marketing restrictions that would otherwise implicate the First Amendment's
free speech protections.[3]

Litigation also provides a critical avenue for recourse when government itself causes
harm, whether by implementing policies that undermine public health goals or by failing
to address systemic injustices. For example, along with state attorneys general, public
health and social justice groups use litigation to fight the rollback of critical public health
protections, such as environmental regulations, or to compel action when governments
fail to comply with regulatory mandates, such as increasing affordable housing or enacting administrative rules. Litigation is particularly important in these instances because
government-inflicted harms often disproportionately affect groups of people without the
political power and resources to change policies through traditional political means.
Indeed, civil rights victories against laws ranging from Jim Crow segregation to voter
disenfranchisement and racial gerrymandering were made possible, at least in part,
through litigation.

Despite these benefits, public health litigation is not without drawbacks. Engaging in
any form of litigation can require substantial financial commitments and legal resources,
and it generally operates on a longer time horizon than policy change through legislative
or administrative action.[2,3] Moreover, public health professionals and advocates might
exercise less control over the outcomes of litigation. Unfavorable litigation outcomes—
whether due to poor legislative drafting, hasty policymaking, or an unfavorable legal
environment—can have substantial consequences. Litigation losses can, for example,
chill political momentum to address an issue and influence legal doctrine in ways that
threaten previous policy successes and future opportunities. These shifts in legal doctrine can be particularly worrisome when they involve constitutional considerations,
such as cases involving the First Amendment or affirmative action. New constitutional
barriers cannot be overcome through political advocacy efforts alone.

Finally, litigation can spur backlash from interest groups or opposing policymakers.[1]
For example, in response to local government lawsuits against the pharmaceutical industry for its role in the overdose crisis, the US Chamber of Commerce has sought to curtail
local authority to engage in affirmative litigation.

CONCLUSION

Like law and policy in general, litigation is neither inherently positive nor negative.
Litigation is merely a tool. It can be misused, undermine public health policies, protect
special interest groups, and increase health inequities.[1] It is, however, an invaluable tool
to ensure that industry and government alike remain accountable for their actions or
inaction.[2,4] Effectively leveraging the power of litigation to advance public health and

equity will require new resources and financial investments. This includes continued and increased funding and other support for jurisdictions defending against legal challenges to innovative public health policies and for the nongovernmental entities that provide strategic guidance and support to those jurisdictions. Public health organizations must also be prepared and funded to engage in affirmative litigation, whether to hold industry actors accountable when government fails to do so or to pursue legal challenges against the government itself.

Educational initiatives and technical assistance are needed to inform public health practitioners and the general public on the role of litigation in protecting and advancing public health and equity, including why and how non-legal professionals can participate in such litigation. These initiatives should also address core legal competencies for public health policymaking, such as constitutional considerations and preemption. Indeed, with litigation likely to play an increasing role as public health addresses the social, structural, and political determinants of health, it is all the more important that public health practitioners understand not only how a policy proposal becomes law but how that law is defended and what legal issues it implicates. Likewise, the role of public health lawyers will continue to expand outside the traditional confines of counsel to include roles related to policy development, advocacy, and the growing practice of legal epidemiology. This will necessitate that public health lawyers have a firm grasp of public health science.

Together, these efforts can help the public health field work toward a broader understanding of how litigation can complement—or complicate—legislative and regulatory interventions. These efforts can help those in public health understand how to draft legislation to minimize potential legal risks and put a jurisdiction in an advantageous position, should litigation occur. These efforts can also instruct on how to use litigation proactively to protect the public's health and positively shape public policy through law.

REFERENCES

1. Rutkow L, Teret SP. Role of state attorneys general in health policy. *JAMA*. 2010;304(12):1377–8.

2. Burris S, Penn M, Berman ML, Holiday TR. *The new public health law: a transdisciplinary approach to practice and advocacy.* New York: Oxford University Press; 2018.

3. Carr D, Davis CS, Rutkow L. Reducing harm through litigation against opioid manufacturers? Lessons from the tobacco wars. *Public Health Reports.* 2018;133(2):207–13.

4. Gostin LO, Wiley LF. *Public health law: power, duty, restraint.* Oakland, CA: University of California Press; 2016.

5. Fraley TD, Stagg K, Parker L, Africk JJ. *Locally mandated tobacco health warnings: an analysis of the federal preemption and speech considerations surrounding local policies regarding tobacco health warnings at the point of sale.* Respiratory Health Association: Tobacco White Paper Series; August 2014.

6. City of Chicago. Warning sign for other tobacco products. 2019. Available at: http://bit.ly/ChicagoTobaccoWarning. Accessed May 7, 2021.

7. Carr D, Adler S, Winig BD, Montez JK. Equity first: conceptualizing a normative framework to assess the role of preemption in public health. *Milbank Q.* 2020;98:131–49.

IV

THREATS TO USING POLICY AS A TOOL FOR PUBLIC HEALTH

Perils of Preemption: When State Laws Conflict With Local Policies

Christiana K. McFarland, PhD, David H. Jernigan, PhD, and
Shelley Hearne, DrPH

Steady employment, quality education, and safe housing are examples of the prerequisites needed for vibrant communities, strong economies, and good health for everyone. Policy is a critical tool for elected officials trying to achieve improvements in these areas, and city leaders have been at the forefront of using policy to improve a community's health. Health-promoting policies—from affordable housing to mandatory sick leave to limitations on tobacco availability and sales—help create communities that enable more access to healthy choices and lifestyles for all residents. However, elected city leaders often are unable to enact policies they deem critical to improving the health of their citizens.

Policy is enacted by federal, state, and local governments—but these laws are not equal. The US Constitution's Supremacy Clause in Article VI establishes that federal law is "the supreme Law of the Land." The doctrine of preemption, which is based on the Supremacy Clause, establishes that federal law preempts any state or local law, even when the laws conflict. States and local governments have a similar relationship, with state law preempting local law even when laws conflict.

DEFINING FLOOR AND CEILING PREEMPTION

Preemption can establish a minimum standard to which all must adhere yet can allow flexibility for surpassing this standard. This is known as floor preemption. States have used floor preemption to meet health challenges while maintaining the ability for cities to address local needs. For example, in 1995 California became the first state to issue a statewide ban on tobacco use in public places, thereby preempting cities from enacting weaker laws. Cities are permitted to strengthen the basic protections—for example, by banning smoking in restaurants and bars and extending protections to public places not identified in the statewide law. As a result of these types of protections, lung cancer rates in California have dropped precipitously and have remained below the national average.[1]

Ceiling preemption, by contrast, establishes a maximum standard that a lower level of government cannot exceed. Ceiling preemption is the more concerning of these two methods because states can use it to invalidate or restrict local authority, limiting policy options available to local jurisdictions. A similar form of action is known as vacuum preemption, which occurs when states prohibit localities from taking any action and avoid setting a specific state standard.[2] Consider trying to build a house if the nails have been taken away—local jurisdictions face a similar prospect when states restrict the tools that cities could potentially use to make improvements. In essence, options for local solutions to local problems are taken off the table.

CITYHEALTH POLICIES AND PREEMPTION

Examining data from CityHealth collected through the end of 2019 helps illuminate the impact of state-level ceiling preemption of local ordinances on community health. CityHealth (discussed in detail in Chapter 6) is an initiative of the de Beaumont Foundation and Kaiser Permanente that each year assesses the presence of nine policies in the nation's 40 largest cities and awards a gold, silver, bronze, or no medal for each policy area and an overall medal for the city. The nine policies are as follows:

- Inclusionary zoning (e.g., affordable housing)
- High-quality pre-K
- Healthy vending
- Safer alcohol sales
- Restaurant grading
- Tobacco 21
- Smoke-free indoor air
- Complete streets
- Earned sick leave

For this analysis of ceiling preemption, instances where state preemption restricts cities from implementing one or more of the CityHealth policies were identified, yielding 55 instances where states either limited or entirely preempted a city's authority to act on health-related policies. Preemptions were identified by city; therefore, one state law was counted multiple times if it had an impact on more than one city included in the analysis.

Overall, cities that are most restricted by preemption are those that need these policies the most: cities that experience lower life expectancy for their poorest populations. Inclusionary zoning (14 cities preempted), earned sick leave (16 cities preempted), curbing tobacco sales to youth (11 cities preempted), and improving public safety by regulating the number and practices of places that sell and serve alcohol (9 cities preempted) were the policies most frequently the subject of preemptive state legislation.

STATE PREEMPTION OF LOCAL HEALTH-PROMOTING POLICIES IS NOT EVENLY DISTRIBUTED

Cities subjected to more preempted policies have a decreased likelihood of achieving gold medal status as defined by CityHealth. Across the eight CityHealth "gold medal" cities of Los Angeles, Chicago, New York, Boston, Dallas, San Antonio, San Francisco, and Seattle—those with the most extensive local health policies in place—there are just five instances of limitations imposed by preemption. Dallas and San Antonio face preemption for inclusionary zoning, New York City has a limited ability to regulate alcohol sales, and Seattle has restrictions for Tobacco 21 and alcohol regulation. By contrast, among the 13 CityHealth bronze medal cities, there are 21 instances of preemption. For example, Wisconsin state law prohibits Milwaukee from action on four of the nine CityHealth policies: inclusionary zoning, healthy food vending, Tobacco 21, and paid sick leave.

CITIES WITH WORSE LIFE EXPECTANCY EXPERIENCE THE MOST PREEMPTED LOCAL POLICIES

State-level studies show that life expectancy is lower in states where preemption is more prevalent.[3] While life expectancy has grown in these states since 1980, it has done so at a lower rate than in states with no preemptions (5.9% compared with 8.1%). Geographic variations in life expectancy have been found to increase as income decreases.[4] When defining geography by using commuting zones (which roughly align with metropolitan areas), life expectancy for upper-income groups does not vary significantly from place to place. Regional variation for life expectancy is greatest among the lowest-earning 20% of the population. Outcomes are more strongly correlated with health behaviors than with access to health care or the quality of that care. Local policy, therefore, is critical to ensuring that healthy lifestyles are available to all.

There is an association between life expectancy and preemption. According to data from 2019, in cities with no preemptions of CityHealth policies, life expectancy was 80.2 years, compared to 79.0 years in cities with one preemption and 78.9 years in cities with two or more preemptions. Other factors that may influence life expectancy do not appear to affect these results. Neither poverty rates nor demographics are strongly associated with preemption. A possible explanation for these health inequities is that while wealthier residents can afford to live healthy lifestyles, lower-income individuals are more dependent on policies to make healthier options available. From encouraging walkable neighborhoods to ensuring access to healthy food, local policies may help close the gap in the choices available to all residents.

PREEMPTION LIMITS A COMMUNITY'S ABILITY TO ADDRESS SPECIFIC LOCAL HEALTH RISKS

Communities experiencing disproportionate burdens of disease should have all available options to achieve improved health. However, these options can be limited by state preemption. To better understand the relationship between preemption and health outcomes, the four most frequently preempted CityHealth policies—inclusionary zoning, earned sick leave, curbing tobacco sales to youth, and regulating the number and practices of places that sell and serve alcohol—can be assessed using related health-outcome indicators. Respectively, these indicators are percent of rent-burdened households, percent of population reporting not seeing a doctor when needed because of cost, smoking rates, and rates of excessive alcohol use.

Inclusionary Zoning

The goal of inclusionary zoning is to address high housing costs by providing affordable housing development in tandem with construction of market-rate units. The US Department of Housing and Urban Development defines rent-burdened households as those that spend more than 30% of their income on monthly rent.[5] Across the 40 cities in the CityHealth study, the percentage of rent-burdened households ranges from 29.8% in Oklahoma City to 51.8% in Los Angeles. By that measure, inclusionary zoning is available to cities with higher-than-average rent burdens; i.e., only four of the 14 instances of preemption affect these high-cost cities.

State and local governments have employed inclusionary housing policies since the 1970s, creating and expanding the availability of below-market-rate units in more than 800 cities.[6] Mandatory inclusionary zoning programs have been shown to generate greater benefits, like expanding the supply of affordable housing. Housing affordability and stability have been recognized as significant determinants of health and well-being. Without an affordable place to call home, families face the financial burden of increased rent or the stress generated by housing insecurity.

Earned Sick Leave

The United States is one of only two industrialized nations without a national requirement for paid sick leave. Among the CityHealth cities, 16 are preempted from mandating that employers offer earned sick leave; 10 of those cities are in states where more than 13% of the population reported not seeing a doctor when needed because of cost.

In 2006, San Francisco became the first US city to implement a mandatory earned sick leave policy after a public referendum passed with 61% in favor. Since then, at least 28 cities have followed suit, and opponents of the policies have turned to state legislatures to preempt mandatory earned sick leave ordinances.[7] As of the end of 2019, 23 states preempt earned sick leave, and many of these preemption laws include additional limitations on regulating health benefits, retirement benefits, or leave benefits, and, in some cases, on enacting fair scheduling requirements.[8]

Workers without earned sick leave are more likely to lose their job because of a medical condition and more likely to skip necessary medical treatment rather than give up a day's pay. These choices disproportionately affect lower-income workers: 64% of private sector workers have access to paid sick leave, but among the bottom quarter of wage earners, only 39% receive this benefit.[9] By requiring employers to provide some measure of sick leave, cities can save workers from the difficult choice between taking care of themselves and getting paid.

Paid sick leave—or the lack of it—received increased attention with the spread of COVID-19. For working Americans without access to paid sick leave, choosing to stay home when sick could mean an inability to buy food, being short on rent, or even losing a job. In response to the COVID-19 pandemic, the federal government passed the Families First Coronavirus Response Act to establish a temporary national requirement for paid sick leave by compelling certain employers to provide employees with paid sick leave or expanded family and medical leave for specified reasons related to COVID-19. These requirements expired at the end of 2020, however, and were not renewed, stripping Americans of access to paid sick leave as the country experienced record COVID-19 hospitalizations and deaths.

Raising the Age to Purchase Tobacco

Although 21 is now the national minimum age for purchase of tobacco products, prior to passage of this law (known as Tobacco 21), analysis of current smoking rates among adults over the age of 18 showed that preempted cities needed this measure the most. Of the 11 CityHealth cities that were prevented from increasing the legal age to purchase tobacco, eight had estimated smoking rates above the 500-city average of 17%, compared with 10 of the 29 cities without such preemption.

Preemption of local tobacco laws—both regulation of sales and use—is the result of one of the first concerted national campaigns waged by an industry to roll back local regulation of its products. Twenty-two states had preemption measures preventing cities from increasing the legal age to purchase tobacco.

While smoking rates were declining across the nation at the turn of the century, public awareness of preemption laws led to some progress for increased local control. Since 2004, seven states have repealed preemption measures that restricted local ordinances on smoke-free indoor air, leaving 12 states with these preemption laws in place. Twenty-seven states have tobacco control laws that allow additional local smoking regulations beyond the state minimum standard. An emerging issue is the regulation of e-cigarettes and vaping products, which typically are not covered by existing legislation.

A slow and steady increase in towns, counties, and cities raising to 21 their minimum age to purchase tobacco products created momentum that culminated in December 2019, when the federal government increased the minimum age for purchasing tobacco products to 21. Nationwide adoption of Tobacco 21 is a testament to the role of localities to test, refine, and showcase effective policy interventions. This experimentation and eventual broad-scale solution was possible only because of the flexibility to pass local policy to address local needs.

Alcohol Sales

Cities can use regulation of alcohol sales as a tool to address a wide range of community health outcomes, including violent crime, injuries, and motor vehicle deaths and disability. Of the nine cities in the analysis of ceiling preemption where alcohol outlet regulation is restricted by exclusive or near-exclusive state preemption, five have higher-than-average rates of excessive alcohol use.

The question of who holds the authority to regulate alcohol sales and outlet density has long been an area of contention between cities and states. State-by-state variation has existed since the repeal of national prohibition in 1933, when the federal government deferred most regulation to the state level. Beginning in the late 1980s, however, as localities began asserting more authority over alcohol sales, industry representatives stepped in and pushed for statewide standards that included preemption language.

The breakdown of state and local control is a complex topic, but according to the Center on Alcohol Marketing and Youth at Boston University, eight states have limited local regulation of alcohol outlet density, four states maintain exclusive licensing control over off-premises outlets only, and 16 states retain exclusive licensing authority with some local regulatory authority.[10] Preempting cities' ability to ensure safer alcohol sales disproportionately affects poorer and Black communities because, across the country, outlets are located primarily in these communities.[11]

COURTING PREEMPTION AND LOCAL HEALTH POLICY

Amid increasing state and federal gridlock, cities have become the primary laboratory for innovative policy solutions. However, with innovation comes increased scrutiny from state legislators and the ever-present threat of preemption. Several cities have attempted to pass policies to make economic or health improvements, only to have those policies challenged by their states.

The risk of preemption cannot deter cities from the difficult but critical work of improving the health of their citizenry through policy. If local progress stalls, cities may continue to suffer from widening gaps in life expectancy, disease rates, and economic vitality between neighborhoods and socioeconomic groups. Bridging these gaps will require cities and states to work together more effectively; if that proves impossible, cities are called to lean into their creativity and innovation to find solutions even within pre-empted policy environments.

REFERENCES

1. Pierce JP, Shi Y, McMenamin SB, et al. Trends in lung cancer and cigarette smoking: California compared to the rest of the United States. *Cancer Prev Res (Phila)*. 2019;12(1):3–12.

2. National League of Cities. Preemption 101. November 2020. Available at: https://www.nlc .org/wp-content/uploads/2020/11/Preemption_101.pdf. Accessed January 27, 2021.

3. Montez JK. Deregulation, devolution, and state preemption laws' impact on US mortality trends. *Am J Public Health*. 2017;107(11):1749–50.

4. Chetty R, Stepner M, Abraham S, et al. The association between income and life expectancy in the United States, 2001-2014. *JAMA*. 2016;315(16):1750–66.

5. US Department of Housing and Urban Development. Affordable housing. Available at: https://www.hud.gov/program_offices/comm_planning/affordablehousing. Accessed March 15, 2019.

6. King, Rebecca. Inclusionary housing policies. Washington, DC: National Low-Income Housing Coalition; 2018.

7. The Henry J. Kaiser Family Foundation. Paid family leave and sick days in the US: findings from the 2017 Kaiser/HRET Employer Health Benefits Survey. October 30, 2017. Available at: https://www.kff.org/womens-health-policy/fact-sheet/paid-family-leave-and-sick-days-in-the-u-s-findings-from-the-2017-kaiserhret-employer-health-benefits-survey. Accessed March 15, 2019.

8. DuPuis, N, Langan T, McFarland C, Panettieri A, and Rainwater B. City rights in an era of preemption: a state-by-state analysis 2018 update. Washington, DC: National League of Cities; 2018.

9. Gould E, Schieder J. Work sick or lose pay? The high cost of being sick when you don't get paid sick days. Economic Policy Institute. June 2017. Available at: https://www.epi.org/publication/work-sick-or-lose-pay-the-high-cost-of-being-sick-when-you-dont-get-paid-sick-days. Accessed March 15, 2019.

10. Center on Alcohol Marketing and Youth. Preemption data tool. Available at: https://wwwapp .bumc.bu.edu/BEDAC_Camy/ResearchToPractice/Place/AlcoholOutletDensity/Preemption DataTool. Accessed July 15, 2021.

11. LaVeist TA, Wallace JM Jr. Health risk and inequitable distribution of liquor stores in African American neighborhood. *Soc Sci Med*. 2000;51(4):613–7.

13

How We Fight With Both Hands and Win

Jake Williams, MS

If you're reading this, a book about improving public health policy, then you're on the team. Maybe you're a student, or a funder, or an advocate, or a public health professional, or just someone who is generally interested in improving the well-being of Americans. Whoever you are, remember that I am telling you this as a teammate. Ready?

We're failing.

While we might argue that things would be even worse if we weren't doing the things we are doing, it clearly isn't anywhere near enough. You can pick just about any public health or social indicator and you'll see that it is abysmal within the context of occurring in the wealthiest, most powerful nation on earth. We don't live as long, or as well, or as equitably as the people within any of our peer group of wealthy nations.

During the COVID-19 pandemic, our underperformance was on full display for the world to see. This had little to do with the level of talent in our public health workforce, from which so many heroes emerged. It had everything to do with how politicians chose to invest in our public health system and utilize public health expertise. Funding for public health budgets is a political issue. Implementing public health decisions to stem a pandemic are political calls. Regard for life, science, or facts themselves are, like it or not, political.

In the United States, the world's largest economy, the public policy process is the only lever powerful enough to create effective change among our 329 million people at a population-level scale. We're not going to solve these problems one person or even one community at a time. That doesn't mean we stop trying to help people at any level we can, it just means that we need to orient our resources and strategy to produce a systemic outcome that gets us out of perpetual disadvantage.

Creating the change we need to heal a nation is an incredible burden to assume, and I guarantee that it is impossible to do if we fight with one hand tied behind our back. We've already got one strong hand in the form of public health expertise, but tied behind us is a hand that could deliver our needed advocacy punch. If we could use both hands in coordination, I believe this team has what it takes to win. Here are my three strategy points on how we do it.

GET THE MONEY YOU NEED

We have a pay-to-play political system in the United States. I am all for reforming it, but until we do, we have to learn how to compete within it. Too often, public health advocates are left waving a literal fact sheet in the middle of a figurative flamethrower fight in city council chambers, state legislatures, and the halls of Congress. Without the resources we need to influence the public policy process, we will continue to be at a disadvantage against competing interests. Now I'm going to tell you the secret of how we get the money we need to compete: We ask for it.

Let me explain further. Think about all the organizations you know that work on public health policy. How much time and energy, if any, are they spending asking for advocacy-eligible money? I'm not saying that raising this money is easy, but I am absolutely saying there is a lack of focus and effort within the public health community in developing this resource.

I spent a period in my career working in the labor movement, where I saw how unions harnessed dues paid by members and converted that money into political power. Public health associations could do the same. There are hundreds of thousands of Americans who work in public health, and many of them belong to public health–oriented associations. Very few are either being asked for political contributions or have those contributions built into their standard dues. For example, the American Public Health Association has 25,000 members. If each member paid $10 per month into a federal political action committee (PAC), they'd have $3 million per year to spend on candidate contributions. That would have made them the third highest spending federal PAC in the United States during the 2020 election cycle.[1]

Associations of health care professionals have been engaging in such practices for a very long time, and they spent a combined $188 million on federal candidates in the 2020 election cycle.[2] If public health professionals want to do something about the political imbalance in power between health care interests and public health, the first step would be to ask for the money they need to compete politically. Health care might always have more financial resources than public health, but that is not a reason to double down on this disadvantage by choosing not to compete at all.

Beyond the public health workforce, there are organizations around the country working to advance public health policy. However, unlike other movements in which I have worked, including the LGBTQ movement and the environmental movement, these organizations often have anemic or nonexistent budgets to engage in lobbying and candidate election advocacy. Part of the reason for this situation is the way in which these organizations interested in public health are funded and the nature of the entities doing the funding.

Think of (or look up) the leading philanthropic foundations that include health among their funding priorities, and then check out their boards and staff. You will find more people with professional histories in philanthropy, government bureaucracy, academia, or practice in a professional health field than you will find those with experience in political campaigns. Now think of (or look up) the leading funding organizations for the environmental or LGBTQ movements and check them out—you'll see many more staff and board members with experience in organizing and political advocacy.

This difference is not an accident, as many philanthropic organizations focused on health do not see political advocacy as something they should be doing or are legally allowed to do. Instead, they focus on things like research, direct service, or community-level solutions of a nonpolitical variety. Often these philanthropies play a mitigating role, one that's aimed at addressing the ills of the system versus changing the system at its root. There are others who do want to take on root issues, like racial injustice, but would never do something like fund an organization to hold elected officials accountable on passing police reform policy or electing more people of color to office.

Cultural change is a precursor to political change, but it is by no means its guarantor. There are many points of view, from stricter gun control, to greater health care access, to tighter campaign finance rules, that have long garnered majority support among Americans but have seen little to no policy action. By all means, it is worth our time to participate in cultural change, but we must also be realistic when assessing the return on investment for a minute or dollar spent echoing a sentiment with public communication versus taking direct political action. There is no shortage of takes delivered in our vast media environment, but there is indeed a scarcity of investment in advocacy for the public interest. Moreover, campaigning for concrete political or policy change is in itself part of cultural change, and is often more likely to get attention due to its tangible consequences.

People in general, not just people in philanthropy (and I've been one of those, too), don't like being told that their prime expertise or resource is not the one that's needed to get the job done. Countering that natural inertia gets even harder when somebody like a foundation officer doesn't have either the information or the impetus to reach beyond the way things have always been done. It is easy to glance at their 501(c)(3) tax status (the same status that these more politically supportive environmental and LGBTQ funders have) and then erroneously claim the legal barriers are too forbidding to support advocacy. It's possible that they're surrounded by people who, like them, have little to no experience in advocacy. Most important, it's likely that their boss or the organization's board is not telling them that this is something that should be explored.

This lack of interest might be due to lack of knowledge or it might be due to the nature of an organization's metrics. It's scary to hold your organization accountable to political or population-level change. It's easier to hold yourself accountable to the number of people who received a particular benefit you directly funded in community "x," or whether you got that playground built in community "y," or whether you got your targeted number of dollars out the door on a particular issue. Boards of directors need to think bigger.

When compared with other movements, health philanthropy in the United States is too modest in scope and accountability, and this feeds a lack of ambition on public policy change. Funders in the LGBTQ movement didn't set out just to make LGBTQ people more "accepted," they sought and continue to seek definitive equality under the law—same as those in the feminist movement. Funders in the environmental movement are on a mission to save the world from climate change, not simply by convincing individuals to alter their behaviors but by actually changing the rules on planet Earth.

If you're a funder who wants to improve public health, I'm asking you to set your metrics to self-destruct. We will all be better off if we are able to create the cultural and political change that would eradicate the need for your existence, at least as your mission is currently construed. It's not that I don't like you (quite the opposite), it's just that other wealthy nations don't have to rely upon charity to keep people in their countries alive and well, and we shouldn't have to either. If you actually believe that health is a human right, then hold yourself accountable to the goal of realizing that right in our democracy.

It won't always be comfortable. I get that when you're a funder, people tend to be nice to you. It's a pleasant place to be—I've been there, I've enjoyed that. This is an influencing social dynamic that shouldn't be underestimated. Taking sides in a political fight raises the risk that maybe people, including people with power, aren't going to be so nice to you. I understand that this is something people (including me) don't exactly welcome, but it is part and parcel of challenging the status quo.

I appreciate that creating public policy change need not rely solely on advocacy-eligible money, particularly as research, organizing, and other cultural change can fuel this activity. At the same time, every successful social movement in the United States has required catalytic or end-goal public policy change, from the Civil Rights Act of 1964 to *Obergefell v. Hodges* in 2015 to the policing reforms we began to see in 2020 as a result of the Black Lives Matter movement. The interests of public health must also embrace this orientation. We can't count on anybody coming to our political rescue. It's not somebody else's job. So, if you're a funder, even one with a tax status that restricts advocacy, then you need to create the opportunity for advocates to ask for the money they need to create the political change we all need.

The methodology for how public charities and private foundations can legally create these opportunities is well-worn territory. Beyond referring you to a helpful resource in the Alliance for Justice's Bolder Advocacy project to learn more, I want to focus on one underreported yet critical capacity that funders can support. Public health advocacy organizations need the ability to successfully ask for the type and volume of money they need to engage in the political process. Whether it comes from small grassroots donations or soliciting money from higher-level individual donors, this is a precious and largely underdeveloped resource.

So, even if you're not a funding organization that can directly deliver money eligible for either lobbying or political candidate activity, you can give general operating grants to organizations that are committed to developing this ability. Raising this type of money is hard. It takes talent and patience, so you need to calibrate your expectations accordingly. However, other movements do this, and ours can, too.

As you'll hear about in the next section, Healthier Colorado gets thousands of small donors to chip in. The only reason we are able to do this is because we had a funding source that gave us the breathing room and the capacity to try. Meanwhile, wealthy donors like those who are interested in underwriting endeavors like schools of public health can also be engaged to use their wealth to create political change within the same issue realm. The same goes for donors who already write checks to complementary political causes. But again, they'll never give us the money until we (skillfully) ask for it.

LEVERAGE YOUR STRENGTHS AND STAY OUT OF YOUR OWN WAY

We live in a participatory democracy, and we are all, at least in theory, asked to make political judgments as individuals. Americans are routinely asked to cast votes on candidates and issues at the local, state, and national levels. Increasingly, the news is reported as punditry and voters are treated as political analysts themselves. Rather than spend time on parsing the policy distinctions between candidates, both media and voters often critique campaign strategy, or the production values of a TV spot, or what the viability of candidates in a primary election will ultimately be in a general election.

This all makes for lively discussion on social media, but it doesn't make you a professional political strategist. I don't mean to artificially elevate what people like me do for a living. In fact, I like to say that politics can be a high calling but that ultimately it is a low art. We often appeal to people's base instincts and use figurative blunt force objects to do so. This reality coexists with the truth that professionalism and talent fundamentally matter when it comes to creating social change.

Well-intentioned public health and health care professionals sometimes overestimate their own political judgment and underestimate the validity of the input provided by professional campaign strategists. I have personally been involved in several situations in which a health professional has asserted a strategy that was ill-advised. In some of those situations our team was able to steer the campaign back on course. In other cases the entire campaign failed as a result.

Health professionals are subject matter experts on health, and while that doesn't automatically make them experts on how to politically advance a policy within their realm of expertise, it does make them a critical part of what is necessarily a team effort. Despite some of the dispiriting news we read today, facts still matter. While facts alone will not necessarily carry the day on advancing evidence-based health policy, being fundamentally correct is a distinct strategic advantage. We'd rather be in the position of peddling reality than having to defend a farce. We need health professionals to inform sound policy proposals, and in many cases they can be instrumental in selling them.

We need the evidence- and reality-based perspectives of people on the front lines of public health, health care, and health research. Decision makers will often give due deference to these professionals in forums like a legislative hearing. Take heart—people tend to like and trust health professionals and support their mission. For nearly two decades, Gallup also has found nurses to be regarded as the most trusted professionals in America.[3] A poll conducted by the Robert Wood Johnson Foundation and the Harvard T.H. Chan School of Public Health in 2021 found that nearly three-quarters of Americans supported "substantially increasing federal spending to improve the nation's public health programs," and the same large majority believes that "the activities of public health agencies are extremely or very important to the health of the nation."[4]

At Healthier Colorado, we're dedicated exclusively to improving public policy, which necessitates the constant consumption of public health research and the consulting of public health experts to inform the policies we pursue. Moreover, we have launched a satellite organization of health professionals, called Healthy Air and Water Colorado, that focuses on engaging the public policy process to address the public health challenges associated with climate change. Combining political talent with public health talent is a potent combination for effective public policy change, so long as everybody on the team allows others to do what they do best.

MEET PEOPLE WHERE THEY ARE

If everybody in the United States had a clear and common understanding of what public health means and what the public health workforce does, then the strategic interests of public health would surely be well served. One of the rare silver linings of the COVID-19 pandemic is that Americans have become more familiar with the role of public health.[4] Most Americans still do not have a nuanced understanding of public health concepts, but that need not be a barrier to making political progress on the items of greatest concern to public health.

I have sat through many focus groups filled with people selected to represent a cross-section of likely voters, and they have little recognition of the professional lingo associated with public health. *Health equity?* Never heard of it. . . . "Does that have to do with the value of my house?" At the same time, people in those same focus groups will demonstrate an understanding of specific issues critical to public health when they are described in plain language. Moreover, polls frequently show strong support for a bold public health agenda. Here is a list of proposals that get support among at least two-thirds of likely voters in my home state of Colorado: banning the sale of flavored tobacco and nicotine products, expunging the records of people previously convicted of marijuana possession, allowing a judge to confiscate guns from a person determined to be a danger to themselves or others, and, during the COVID-19 pandemic, requiring the wearing of masks in public spaces.

These are results seen not just in the laboratory of opinion research but on the streets . . . and I do mean on the streets. Healthier Colorado runs a full-time canvass in which fundraisers engage passersby on the street on a wide variety of public health issues and then ask them to donate money—and these passersby do it. They not only do it once, the majority of those who donate actually commit to having a recurring monthly donation charged to their credit card.

Healthier Colorado literally and figuratively meets people where they are. We find them on the street, or at an organizing event, or online, and then we do our best to use accessible, compelling language to activate them in support of our pro-health agenda. Some of the language we use is drawn from opinion research, some of it is honed from "A versus B" online testing, and some of it is developed through constant conversation on the street. We don't get it right every time, but we've done well enough to get people to take over 200,000 actions that reached a decision maker—like signing an online petition, or making a phone call, or showing up to a town hall meeting—in the past year alone.

The people who take these actions and the elected officials who are influenced by them don't belong to just one political party. We've met people where they are in the Democratic Party, the Republican Party, and outside any party, and they've actually listened. A key component of our theory of change is that by authentically wielding political carrots (we've financially supported candidates in both parties) and sticks (we've publicly called out elected officials in both parties) according to an elected official's alignment with our agenda, regardless of party or where they stand on other issues, we can create a durable, bipartisan, pro-health coalition. It's working. One proof point: every piece of priority legislation we helped pass in the state legislature last year had bipartisan support, even though Democrats now control both chambers of the legislature and the governor's office.

Healthier Colorado's achievements have included ending state preemption on local tobacco control; instituting universal access to preschool; passing the nation's second-ever voter-approved sugary drinks tax; ending the issuing of predatory "payday loans"; raising nutrition, screen time, and physical activity standards in our state's child care centers; expanding the availability of free and reduced lunch in schools; raising significantly the minimum wage in Denver; stopping the statewide practice of putting innocent people experiencing a mental health crisis in jail; expanding the availability of rural broadband; subsidizing the cost of health insurance premiums for people without documentation; and instituting one of the most robust paid sick leave laws in the country. Plus, we've contributed to the victories of over 30 local ballot measures in the past four years. We've met people where they are on a very wide range of issues, and they've responded with action that has changed lives for the better across our entire population here in Colorado.

We're not perfect, but I truly believe that the lessons we've learned at Healthier Colorado can and should be exported across America. We shouldn't be the only advocacy organization in the country engaging in the full range of available advocacy tactics—from grassroots organizing to lobbying to engaging in candidate elections—in the interest of public health. That's why, as a member of the same team you're on, I sincerely hope you embrace these strategic recommendations so we can all start fighting together for the well-being of Americans without one hand tied behind our back.

REFERENCES

1. Center for Responsive Politics. Top PACs giving to candidates, 2019–2020. Available at: https://www.opensecrets.org/political-action-committees-pacs/2020. Accessed May 3, 2021.

2. Center for Responsive Politics. Industry profile: health professionals. Available at: https://www.opensecrets.org/federal-lobbying/industries/summary?cycle=2020&id=H01. Accessed May 3, 2021.

3. Gaines K. Nurses ranked most trusted profession 19 years in a row. January 6, 2020. Available at: https://nurse.org/articles/nursing-ranked-most-honest-profession/. Accessed May 17, 2021.

4. Robert Wood Johnson Foundation and Harvard T.S. Chan School of Public Health. The public's perspective on the United States public health system. May 13, 2021. Available at: https://cdn1.sph.harvard.edu/wp-content/uploads/sites/94/2021/05/RWJF-Harvard-Report_FINAL-051321.pdf. Accessed May 17, 2021.

V

ADVOCACY IN ACTION

14

You Don't Ask, You Don't Get: A Case Study in Building Coalitions for Public Health Funding

Emily J. Holubowich, MPP

Data are the cornerstone of public health. Public health surveillance—the continuous, systemic collection and interpretation of these health-related data to plan, implement, and evaluate public health interventions[1]—protects the public from health threats of all kinds, including re-emerging vaccine-preventable diseases like measles, emerging infectious diseases like Ebola and Zika, and new threats such as opioid misuse, e-cigarettes, natural disasters, and more.[2]

COVID-19 has shone a bright light on America's systemic failures in both health care and public health in general, and its woefully inadequate data infrastructure in particular. Public health professionals have long recognized the challenges and dangers of our error-prone, sluggish, and burdensome manual and paper-based data exchange, but the pandemic has brought widespread, national attention to just how broken it is and why having timely, accurate, complete data matters.[3] Examples such as public health professionals taking photos of lab reports and texting them to colleagues, physicians being pulled away from patient care to fax case reports to public health departments, and coroners carrying paper death certificates to physicians to certify cause of death are the norm rather than the exception. Indeed, these work-arounds are often the only way to collect and transmit vital health data. Such inefficiencies create delays and inaccuracies in reporting and waste valuable time. In public health, time translates into lives saved. When the data move slower than disease,[4] public health professionals and policymakers are unable to effectively protect people and lives are lost.

The sad state of public health surveillance in the United States is a direct result of policymakers' failure to prioritize it and fund modernization efforts. Until very recently, policymakers have provided surveillance funding in a piecemeal approach, if at all. For example, the Health Information Technology for Economic and Clinical Health (HITECH) Act—enacted as part of the American Recovery and Reinvestment Act of 2009—included a $40 billion investment to implement electronic health records in the health care sector. Public health departments were not provided any funding under the HITECH Act to modernize their systems to fully optimize data exchange between health care and public health, exacerbating fragmentation and increasing administrative burden on health care providers and public health professionals alike. Without direct, meaningful funding, the data modernization efforts to date of some systems in some jurisdictions have largely been supported by emergency supplemental funding to address public health crises. Even then, most of these efforts have been prioritized at the discretion of public health professionals who have seen the dire need and potentially calamitous consequences of antiquated systems—and not at the explicit direction of policymakers who control the purse strings.

But policymakers don't bear all the blame. To make informed decisions about where and how to invest finite resources, policymakers need information and they need to know a problem exists. For too long, the public health community didn't effectively speak truth to power with one voice about the nation's data needs. Policymakers heard about stakeholders' data concerns and frustrations in a fragmented, piecemeal way—disease by disease. And so they addressed these concerns by funding data collection "systems" disease by disease, often outbreak by outbreak. The efforts further fragmented data collection and the entrenched status quo without addressing the underlying issues through an enterprise-wide approach.

Unfortunately, as the COVID-19 pandemic rages on, there remains no question among policymakers and the public that the public health surveillance infrastructure must move from 20th-century methods—paper records, manual data entry, and fax machines—that hinder evidence-based decision-making to a 21st-century enterprise that uses technology to facilitate automatic, real-time, interoperable, secure data exchange. A coordinated effort to raise awareness about the deficiencies and risks of the crumbling data infrastructure and secure long overdue funding for modernization began in earnest three years ago. The early success of this effort—and its continued success today—demonstrates what's possible when the public health community is willing to mobilize en masse and is unafraid to communicate its needs publicly. It serves as a case study for others looking to build coalitions to fund public health.

STEP 1: DEFINE THE PROBLEM AND PROPOSE A SOLUTION

In 2019, with support from the de Beaumont Foundation, the Council of State and Territorial Health Epidemiologists (CSTE) published a now eerily prescient report documenting the long-standing challenges of the public health surveillance infrastructure and the impact on the public's health and safety, articulating a vision for a fully interoperable public health data enterprise. "Driving Public Health in the *Fast* Lane: The Urgent Need for a 21st Century Public Health Data Superhighway"[2] included testimonials from key stakeholders in the public and private sectors who shared real-world stories from the field and demonstrated proof of concept for proposed improvements. For example, the report featured partners from "Digital Bridge"—a public-private forum for leaders in public health, health care, and health information technology (HIT) who convened on issues of electronic data sharing—that provided evidence from pilots on electronic case reporting in several jurisdictions and demonstrated that seamless data exchange was possible.

The report also recommended principles for data modernization and provided a roadmap to improve systems at the federal, state, local, territorial, and tribal levels. It emphasized the need to recruit, train, and retain a qualified workforce with the skills to maintain and use new technology, as well as the need to move the resulting data into action. In articulating the what, why, and how, the report provided the foundation for a broader advocacy campaign and served as the North Star to guide those efforts.

STEP 2: BUILD PARTNERSHIPS AND RECRUIT CHAMPIONS

Identifying "who" is a critical step in any advocacy campaign—arguably the most important. Who will lead and set the table? Who must be at the table? Who are the policymakers who will champion the cause? Who are the opponents, and how hard will they fight to stop forward progress?

CSTE, the Association of Public Health Laboratories (APHL), and the National Association for Public Health Statistics and Information Systems (NAPHSIS)—the principal stewards of public health data at the state and local level—and the Healthcare Information and Management Systems Society (HIMSS) represent the private sector and both HIT vendors and health care providers. They formed a partnership to launch the Data: Elemental to Health advocacy campaign to translate the "Driving Public Health in the *Fast* Lane" report's vision to policymakers and stakeholders, and move its recommendations toward policy. Specifically, the campaign sought $1 billion in new federal funding over 10 years for the Centers for Disease Control and Prevention (CDC) to modernize its public health surveillance infrastructure and that of public health agencies at the federal, state, local, territorial, and tribal levels, and to invest in the public health workforce of the future.

The partners were careful to consider whose support they would need for their advocacy effort to be successful. They spent months "lobbying the lobbyists" across the public health, health care provider, HIT, and patient communities to build a consensus for the data modernization initiative and to recruit a coalition of advocates to join the campaign. Across this diverse constituency, there was a shared frustration with the status quo, a shared need for more, better, and faster public health data, and a shared appreciation for the need to work together to influence change. Ultimately, the campaign mobilized the support of more than 100 national organizations across myriad special interests to work in concert in support of the $1 billion funding request of Congress.

The group also spent significant time identifying and cultivating influential champions in positions of power who could carry the request forward. Through many strategic, thoughtful conversations—involving more listening than talking—the campaign was able to excite congressional policymakers on both sides of the aisle and at the highest levels of CDC leadership. The support of these champions was essential for building broader support for data modernization and to thwart efforts to undermine the campaign's progress.

STEP 3: DON'T LET A CRISIS GO TO WASTE

So much of success in advocacy is about having the right people in the right place at the right time. Indeed, timing is everything in policymaking, and the unfortunate reality is that a public health crisis is often needed to grab policymakers' attention and move them to act. The Data: Elemental to Health campaign launched in the aftermath of the Zika outbreak, during which the nation's data infrastructure challenges were on full display. Policymakers who were previously unaware of the data challenges were inundated with calls and mail from fearful constituents seeking more information about the virus. They learned quickly that public health was ill-equipped to provide up-to-date, accurate information. The same was true for the ongoing opioid crisis, during which policymakers were frustrated by the lack of timely data about overdoses and deaths as they attempted to formulate a meaningful policy response and face concerned constituents back home. Coalition partners used these timely crises, as well as the national outbreak of e-cigarette or vaping product use–associated lung injury that occurred in the midst of the campaign, to make the case that more timely, complete, and accurate data would help policymakers be more responsive to their constituents' needs and inform their policy decisions.

Because of these crises, policymakers were well aware of the data challenges because they had experienced them firsthand. They just didn't understand why they didn't have the data they wanted when they wanted them, or how they could fix the system to get them. The coalition partners had to connect the dots and educate them about the challenges and solutions through countless face-to-face meetings, earned and social media, phone calls, letters, and congressional testimony.

ADVOCACY WORKS: DATA MODERNIZATION INITIATIVE RECEIVES MUCH NEEDED FUNDING

The Data: Elemental to Health campaign resulted in a huge win for public health data advocates everywhere. By the end of 2019, appropriations legislation was signed into law that included $50 million in new funding for the CDC's data modernization initiative— the first such funding for an enterprise approach to data collection. In addition, four authorizing bills supporting public health data modernization that would codify the data modernization initiative into law were introduced in both chambers of Congress with bipartisan support. Since then, the COVID-19 pandemic has only heightened awareness about the urgent need for more, better, faster data—and the dire, deadly consequences of maintaining the status quo. Because of groundwork laid by the campaign prior to the pandemic, Congress now understands what must be done to move forward and has appropriated another $1 billion for public health surveillance improvements through the Coronavirus Aid, Relief, and Economic Security (CARES) Act and the American Rescue Plan Act.

It is exciting to envision a future in which public health can not only rapidly respond to public health threats as they emerge but also use predictive analytics to detect threats and act to prevent them before they begin to spread. But public health advocates must not become complacent. The Data: Elemental to Health campaign was successful because public health professionals, together with health care providers and patients, were willing to speak up about not just public health's successes but its shortcomings as well. Public health professionals must be willing to engage in advocacy and tell their stories—the good, the bad, and the ugly—to anyone and everyone who will listen. The Data: Elemental to Health campaign shows what is possible when we raise our voices, and do so loudly, for the sake of public health.

REFERENCES

1. World Health Organization. Public health surveillance. Available at: https://www.who.int/immunization/monitoring_surveillance/burden/vpd/en. Accessed September 30, 2020.

2. Hagan CN, Holubowich EJ, Criss T. Driving Public health in the *fast* lane: the urgent need for a 21st century data superhighway. Council of State and Territorial Epidemiologists; 2019. Available at: https://www.debeaumont.org/wp-content/uploads/2019/09/DSI-White-Paper_v15-Spreads.pdf. Accessed April 16, 2021.

3. Kliff S, Sanger-Katz M. Bottleneck for US coronavirus response: the fax machine. *The New York Times*. Published July 13, 2020. Available at: https://www.nytimes.com/2020/07/13/upshot/coronavirus-response-fax-machines.html. Accessed April 16, 2021.

4. Hamilton J. Oral testimony: Education Public Witness Day hosted by the Subcommittee on the Departments of Labor, Health and Human Services, Education, and Related Agencies. April 9, 2019; Washington, DC. Available at: https://www.youtube.com/watch?v=KGRHg-840KE&feature=youtu.be&t=12456. Accessed April 16, 2021.

15

#SpeakForHealth

Susan L. Polan, PhD

Troubling rumors had been percolating. Then, on December 15, 2017, a *Washington Post* headline confirmed our concerns: "CDC gets list of forbidden words: Fetus, transgender, diversity."[1] Public health agencies were being gagged.

The American Public Health Association (APHA) staffs the Centers for Disease Control and Prevention (CDC) Coalition, a nonpartisan partnership of organizations committed to strengthening our nation's public health infrastructure and prevention programs. APHA has long been the primary association focusing on the big picture in support of funding for CDC, and so APHA staff immediately began gathering information to better understand the policy and funding implications of this new directive.

All roads led to the same conclusion: CDC budget analysts were being censored.

Words like "vulnerable," "entitlement," "diversity," "transgender," "fetus," "evidence-based," and "science-based"—terms that are critical to understanding and practicing public health—were being removed from descriptions of the CDC's work. Theoretically, the suggested language changes would improve chances of gaining funding for programs that could be considered controversial in a deeply partisan and science-averse Congress.

But moving from evidence-based decision-making to having the "CDC [base] its recommendations on science in consideration with community standards and wishes" is a substantive change that provoked outrage throughout the public health and science communities. Adding a "community standards and wishes" clause seemed like a minor change to many, but the attack on sound, evidence-based policy was subtle yet clear, and the implications on policy implementation could be huge. For example, vaccine requirements for school-age children could be weakened if community standards were given equal weight as science and evidence. Access to the full scope of reproductive services for all pregnant women could be undermined. APHA staff had the same concern and worked to define a response in the few days before everyone scattered for the holiday break. #SpeakForHealth was born.

Around the same time, two additional events created the perfect confluence of concern to encourage people to engage in conversation to protect their health. New data were released that showed a decline in life expectancy in the United States for the second year in a row,[2] and a bill further undermining the Affordable Care Act was set to be signed.

All of these issues had to be addressed. But the general public and the public health community needed to think beyond their own silos and understand the connections of these three seemingly disparate events.

To be effective, we required a coordinated campaign with a unifying theme, one that involved more than just APHA and our advocates. It was time for the public to get involved. Everyone who cared about creating healthy people and healthy communities had to be energized. The driving goal of #SpeakForHealth was to engage public health professionals and the public in a communications campaign to foster better understanding of the value and the role of public health. We needed to stop talking to ourselves and become more comfortable engaging in public health policy discussions by bringing both our expertise and lived experience to the policy table.

All of this was happening in a broader cultural context. Most people simply don't know what "public health" is or what it does to keep them safe every single day. The agenda is wide-ranging; the connection between interventions and outcomes is often hard to see; the field is crowded with organizations demanding the limited time and attention of the public; and there are organizations with competing interests that use the language of public health but have more specific messages. It all results in misperception.

The umbrella of public health is broad and silent. How all people in every community benefited from the work of public health professionals is misunderstood as health care for the indigent, emergency preparedness, vaccinations, or worksite wellness. Breaking through these persistent misrepresentations is a real challenge.

When the nation's primary public health agency was being censored and people were dying from completely preventable illnesses and conditions, we needed to activate the public to support work they didn't even know existed.

A few years earlier, APHA leadership had approved a strategic plan to create "the healthiest nation in one generation." A critical piece of this goal was engaging people beyond APHA's members, caucuses, and affiliates. Starting with public health professionals and building outward, a new group of people needed to be educated about the work of public health and the importance of advocating on its behalf. APHA was working on creating that movement—called "Generation Public Health"—before the CDC fell under what both the media[3] and policymakers[4] labeled a gag order.

#SpeakForHealth was the first attempt to reenergize this nascent movement into a voice for protecting the broad spectrum of public health and its science- and evidence-based approaches. We set out to give public health professionals a set of tools and engagement materials to respond to challenges communities were facing: the opioid crisis, obesity, chronic illness, tobacco use, and rising e-cigarette and vaping problems. With limited funds available, email and social media would be the primary mechanism for distributing information. And while APHA has a robust social media presence and a thriving Twitter feed, there were few public health stars with a blue check of verification engaging in far-ranging discussions of the social determinants of health.

#SpeakForHealth was a rallying cry to encourage APHA members, Generation Public Health, and the public to make their voices heard. It was an invitation to be part of a larger movement celebrating public health work and addressing health problems in communities all over the country. This new platform was designed as an easy channel for people to express their support for public health and to communicate the important work APHA does to protect our communities. Whereas previous social media campaigns—such as "This Is Public Health"—were mostly about educating the public, #SpeakForHealth was designed to inspire action.

The first step was to encourage people to post a photo on social media with a #SpeakForHealth sign and an explanation of why they support public health and why our efforts cannot be silenced. The response was instantaneous. Individuals and organizations started using the hashtag to highlight their work, why they believed it was important, what their friends and colleagues should know, and why opinion-makers and policy leaders should be concerned about attacks on public health and health care.

Over time, APHA staff created more tools and opportunities to engage members and Generation Public Health in #SpeakForHealth. Leveraging existing events like our summer grassroots advocacy efforts, National Public Health Week, and the APHA Annual Meeting allowed us to build a broad following and expand the reach of the campaign. The goal always was to influence and improve public health policy.

In 2018, we expanded #SpeakforHealth by offering the inaugural Student Bootcamp, engaging the next generation of leaders in public health advocacy. An intense two-day event, it brought together close to 100 students who heard from experts about the connection between climate change and health. After a day of training, this informed and engaged group took the #SpeakForHealth message to their federal representatives. We convened nearly 200 students for a second successful Student Bootcamp in 2019.

That same year, APHA organized its first Policy Action Institute, entitled Public Health Under Siege: Improving Policy in Turbulent Times. The event gave professionals and students an opportunity to hear leaders in public health, government, and advocacy discuss common issues, opportunities, and strategies to address the nation's biggest health challenges at city, state, and federal levels. The 2020 Policy Action Institute, All Hands on Deck: Improving Community Health, again featured interactions with elected leaders, policy experts, and other influential speakers. Participants addressed the social determinants of health—access to care, education, transportation, and environmental health—as well as discrimination and income inequality.

The goal of the Policy Action Institute is to arm public health professionals with practical ways to implement effective policy at all levels and to open a dialogue about the roles and goals of public health, leading to the ability to advocate in any setting. They are another important lever in the #SpeakForHealth campaign.

But challenges persist. For all the strides we have made in engaging APHA members, public health partners, and Generation Public Health, there are obstacles to moving people to action. Highlighting the work of public health professionals is one thing; inspiring targeted champions and the public toward greater advocacy is another. Strong public health policy has to be generated on the basis of science and evidence, but it has to be moved by stories and public support. As a community we have not consistently employed the modern tools of pithy messages, storytelling, and social media shareables to influence policy and policymakers. Having champions—including members of Congress, governors, state legislators, mayors, and other elected officials—in the right places is critical. But it is not enough. Being able to tell a compelling story to make the abstract and vast world of public health relevant to some of the moneyed interests in politics and the people on the street are equally important variables that require different skill sets. The arena is very crowded, and people may feel overwhelmed by the broad scope of the field, some of which might not seem related to their daily work, personal lives, courses of study, or understanding of what issues are relevant.

"Public health" is hard to define, and vague descriptions often simply confuse. The focus on equity and health in all public policies allows public health professionals to address the true components of health. But this focus also creates a diffuse and, for some, only loosely connected network of issues. Using social media to highlight the diverse and important work of public health without the resources to break down silos and reservations is a continuing challenge.

The public health community should continue to take advantage of low-cost opportunities to amplify its message. But we must also address self-censorship, which is often driven by fear among public health professionals and can manifest in many ways, such as

- concern that as government employees they cannot engage in advocacy as private citizens when they are off duty;
- a lack of understanding about the difference between advocacy and lobbying;
- discomfort with individual self-promotion and with putting the field in the spotlight; and
- a lack of recognition that much of public health is political and that policy is a critical tool.

Public health professionals and the general public alike must step outside their comfort zones and speak up. No gag rule—whether publicly issued by an anti-science administration or self-imposed by a limiting culture—can be allowed to survive if we are to succeed in our professional calling or reach our societal potential. There are a variety of tools and resources readily available to help public health professionals and nonprofit leaders better understand how to engage in these important policy discussions.[5]

This will also require resources to train the public health field—starting while future professionals are still in school—in communications, storytelling, advocacy, and expressing complex work in digestible messages. The general public should be the new force of public health advocates, led by those who effectively share the message of creating the healthiest nation in one generation.

If we are to succeed, we must all learn to #SpeakForHealth.

Acknowledgments: Thanks to Joe Center and Joe Bremner for comments and edits.

REFERENCES

1. Sun LH, Eilperin J. CDC gets list of forbidden words: fetus, transgender, diversity. *The Washington Post.* December 15, 2017. Available at: https://www.washingtonpost.com/national/health-science/cdc-gets-list-of-forbidden-words-fetus-transgender-diversity/2017/12/15/f503837a-e1cf-11e7-89e8-edec16379010_story.html. Accessed September 21, 2020.

2. Khazan O. A shocking decline in American life expectancy. *The Atlantic.* December 21, 2017. Available at: https://www.theatlantic.com/health/archive/2017/12/life-expectancy/548981/. Accessed September 28, 2020.

3. Ramsey D. Trump administration gag order at CDC: forbidden words include "fetus," "transgender," "evidence-based," "diversity." *Arkansas Times.* December 16, 2017. Available at: https://newstral.com/en/article/en/1082712480/gag-order-at-the-cdc-forbidden-words-include-fetus-transgender-evidence-based-diversity. Accessed September 21, 2020.

4. Durbin blasts Trump administration for reported list of seven forbidden words. Dick Durbin: United States Senator, Illinois. December 18, 2017. Available at: https://www.durbin.senate.gov/newsroom/press-releases/durbin-blasts-trump-administration-for-reported-list-of-seven-forbidden-words. Accessed September 21, 2020.

5. Bolder Advocacy. Resource Library. Available at: https://bolderadvocacy.org/resource-library. Accessed September 21, 2020.

16

Embracing Incrementalism

Patrick Guerriero

Incrementalism is one of the most transformative strategies any advocacy effort can choose. Advocates working on many critical challenges facing our country have wasted precious time and energy debating the false choice between fighting for transformative change versus embracing the principles of incrementalism. It is actually possible, even strategically important, to choose both!

Over the past three decades, as former mayor of my hometown, state legislator, and leader of national advocacy campaigns and organizations, I have seen the best and worst of winning and losing advocacy initiatives. Some of the most powerful lessons I learned were from extensive work in support of the groundbreaking efforts by the lesbian, gay, bisexual, and transgender (LGBT) movement to enact state laws on nondiscrimination and relationship recognition, including marriage equality. This work was a critical piece of the political and policy puzzle, which bolstered the successful legal strategy that secured marriage equality and nondiscrimination through rulings of the US Supreme Court.

After decades of truly courageous advocacy, the LGBT movement woke up the morning after the 2004 election facing the grim reality that it was failing badly. The majority of states had banned same-sex marriage; there were no federal laws protecting LGBT people from hate crimes or discrimination; gays and lesbians weren't allowed to serve openly in the US military; and the general public was reluctant to support full equality, especially when given a choice in the privacy of the voting booth.

It was a gut-wrenching, soul-searching period that forced us to rethink every aspect of our strategy. It was noble and just to believe in immediate and unconditional equality for every American regardless of sexual orientation, but we knew only a tough incremental slog could make that a reality.

WINNING FOR A CHANGE

The first task was to secure victories—one person, one company, one community, one city, one state at a time. Cities, states, and corporations are great incubators of innovation and experimentation, and they offered a playing field where we could effect change. That strategic pivot shaped the winning, multiyear formula of securing marriage victories through legislatures, ballot boxes, and the courts in a set of geographically, demographically, and politically diverse states across the country—from Iowa to Hawaii and from Minnesota to Maine. While there were hard losses along the way, the political and public momentum created by each state win led the US Supreme Court to eventually consider and grant nationwide marriage equality in 2015. By design, a set of incremental wins led to a historic national victory.

FINDING A MESSAGE THAT RESONATES

To put it bluntly, the LGBT movement spent a lot of time and money using advocacy messaging that did not work. We were talking to ourselves. The movement had to change the way it communicated. Our messaging had highlighted the harms being done to gay and lesbian couples—the conversation was about the 1,324 rights and responsibilities being denied to gay and lesbian couples each day. But this did not resonate with an audience of mostly straight decision-makers and voters who had to be persuaded before any real progress could be made.

To appeal to a broader audience, the movement's messaging was realigned to meet the audience "where they were" by appealing to their existing values and utilizing the way they talked about their own marriages. Thus, the narrative became about the love and commitment all couples have for each other and less about the benefits afforded to those couples. Critically, these were not one-time strategic or tactical changes but changes that evolved as the movement learned from one battle to the next.

A similar challenge is facing public health advocates today. Most Americans have only experienced the highly political and highly partisan debates over health policy. Those messages fall flat with most Americans. The health sector has an opportunity to adapt its message so it connects with a broad spectrum of people, but it will need to invest the time and resources to meet them "where they are."

Imagine a health care system that is informed by what Americans want and need rather than what has been gradually carved out by special interests. We would be more likely to see people-centered policies and practices and an increased focus on important issues that are too often overlooked. Not only does winning require a shift in the way we are thinking about the policies that are being prioritized, it also requires a shift in how we're talking about health care. Our health is an immensely personal thing, and effectively connecting with Americans in an emotionally resonant manner could dramatically improve the call for change.

WORKING ACROSS THE AISLE

A reality of our political system is that if you want to secure and maintain policy wins, you need to build a bipartisan firewall. This was a vulnerability for LGBT advocates, who had successfully established LGBT equality as a central tenet of the Democratic Party while paying lip service to bipartisan outreach. The resistance to Republican outreach was understandable given that many on the far right had spent years as unrelenting opponents to equality. However, as we began to build advocacy campaigns across the country, it became clear that bipartisan messaging, validators, and supporters were going to be needed to win over policymakers and the public. In so many of these historic and momentum-building wins from coast to coast, it was a mix of Democrats *and* Republicans that helped us across the finish line. This shift to a more incremental, bipartisan, state-by-state approach allowed us to finally break through and effect change in red, blue, and purple states.

As we have seen in so many of the national health care battles, extreme partisanship poisons the policy discussion. Even when big legislative wins happen, the partisan nature of those federal debates jeopardizes the sustainability of policy advances. The tactics used to win policy fights along party lines may seem sufficient for the short-term but are detrimental over the long haul. As the public health sector shapes the next generation of advocacy, finding ways to bridge the partisan divide between elected officials and citizens will be paramount to lasting success.

KNOWING YOUR OPPONENTS

Focusing on specific states and regions to turn the tide for LGBT Americans also gave us the chance to better identify, study, expose, and eventually defeat our opponents. We were often asked, "Are there really people waking up each morning focusing on defeating policies to end discrimination against gay people?" The answer was a resounding "Yes!" Those stealthy opponents were well funded and well organized, and they successfully marketed themselves simply as champions of family values and traditional marriage. By putting a spotlight on the people running these organizations, disclosing who was funding them, and exposing their history of hateful rhetoric, we made average Americans feel less comfortable siding with—and more importantly, voting with—these organizations.

We can similarly ask, "Who could be opposed to every American having access to health care? Who wakes up each day working to deny persons with mental health challenges access to real support? Who really works to limit access to comprehensive care for poor women in America?" Once you know who your opponents are, it's easier to tell the full story of their financial and political interests.

PLAYING OFFENSE

For many years our opponents aggressively controlled where and when anti-gay legislative and ballot fights would be waged, giving themselves the home-field advantage in every fight. As we grew smarter, we began identifying states where we could win and tailored our advocacy efforts around which aspect of LGBT family recognition each state was ready for—civil unions or marriage equality.

An often overlooked but powerful element of an incremental strategy is the impact it has on advocates when they win. As movements develop the right mix of strategies, tactics, messages, and relationships to win the small victories, something especially important happens—they become better equipped for the big fights! LGBT advocates in Iowa started by passing safe schools legislation and building crucial relationships and skills that were then used to pass nondiscrimination legislation. By the time marriage equality came via the state's supreme court, LGBT advocates had built the relationships and political muscle to block its repeal. Winning begets winning, and you get better at it with experience.

BUILDING REAL POWER

Finally, winning requires real champions and the ability to hold both friends and opponents accountable. We have seen organizations like the National Rifle Association and the American Israel Public Affairs Committee master this strategy of setting a high bar for support and calling out elected officials for even the slightest betrayal. For many years, the LGBT movement's political friends talked about their support at black-tie dinners and fundraisers, but when our basic rights were on the line, those friends were too often silent and sometimes even willing to vote against us. Until we held these leaders accountable, we had no real power. You know you've built real power when politicians put your cause before other policy priorities and when they are willing to stand with you despite the political consequences.

Health advocates have many good friends but will need even more robust and dependable champions as we continue to advocate for and win policy victories at the local, state, and national levels—something our country needs now more than ever.

17

Ensuring Policy Impact Through Strong Legal Practice

Marice Ashe, JD, MPH

Laws and policies in areas that seemingly have nothing to do with community health—land use planning, home mortgage lending, school financing, design and enforcement of criminal laws, and many others—are actually social determinants of health that sharply influence community health outcomes. So many current health inequities are born from multiple generations of discriminatory laws and policies that trace their roots to historic injustices, such as slavery and its aftermath and the multiple waves of anti-immigrant legislation enacted since our nation was founded.

The biggest challenge to reversing such systematic injustice is creating the political will to rectify this legacy.[1] The BUILD Health Challenge and other similar efforts have focused on identifying, nurturing, and empowering community champions to create a power base for demanding the necessary legislative and regulatory changes to rectify past harms and lay a course for an equitable future. The good news: we know these community-led collective efforts, which build social capital and focus policy change efforts, actually work to improve health outcomes and address inequities.[2]

To maximize the effectiveness of community champions, their efforts need to be matched with strong legal practice, so advocacy focuses on laws and policies specifically designed for effectiveness in addressing health inequities. Health equity goals can be achieved most quickly by strategically combining community-based leadership with a laser focus on the quality of the laws and policies community champions are advocating for and passing.

The following guidelines outline opportunities for community champions to advocate for quality laws and policies and thereby maximize the effectiveness of their advocacy campaigns. The guidelines can be used as a checklist when developing and evaluating advocacy targets or proposing changes to new or existing laws and policies.

1. **Ground action in public health principles**: As a baseline, core principles drawn from exemplary public health practice should inform the work of advocacy campaigns.
   a. **Evidence base**: Legal and policy campaigns must be grounded in strong science or in emerging best practices when strong science is not yet available. Traditional evidence such as that found in scientific journals can be combined with evidence from the experience of communities living with injustices.

b. **Community engagement**: The adage "nothing about us without us" is especially pertinent in relation to law and policy campaigns designed to have powerful effects on community health. Leadership from, ownership by, and partnership with affected communities is essential.

c. **Focus on social determinants of health**: Community champions can maximize their advocacy efforts by focusing on the social determinants of health, such as how public and private goods are created, accessed, or distributed. Changes to these structures of civic life will have the most long-term impact on community health.

Practice tip: Campaigns with strong public health practice norms will have a foundation for success.

2. **Draft laws to address inequities explicitly**: Careful drafting of laws and policies is critical to success. At the very outset, advocates can frame laws and policies to explicitly state an intention to redress inequities in income, civil and economic rights, and other social determinants of health. Strong legislation includes a "Findings" section that can feature both quantitative and qualitative evidence to frame the purpose and intent of the legislation. Champions can ensure that both traditional science and community-generated evidence is part of the legislative record. Additionally, the "Definitions" section of a law ought to use clear and unambiguous language so that key terms and priorities are stated with precision to ensure the new law is implemented as intended by the community champions. Finally, legislation can require meaningful mechanisms for ongoing community engagement via monitoring, reporting, and evaluation protocols so that community champions can become watchdogs and know if their legislative goals are being met in a timely manner. (See #4 and #7)

Practice tip: Care at the drafting stage of the legislative process will create the potential for community champions to be effective watchdogs for policy success. Additionally, if the legislation is ever challenged via litigation, the explicit language in the legislation regarding health equity will guide a court in how to interpret the law in the best light of the advocacy goals.

3. **Fund implementation**: Simply put, if there isn't funding for the law, nothing will happen. Sadly, there are countless examples of feel-good resolutions and aspirational laws and policies that fail to create any change whatsoever because no funding mechanism is ever identified to bring the good ideas to fruition. Typical funding mechanisms are taxes (e.g., sales, excise, property, income, etc.), fees (e.g., licenses, permits, building, use, etc.), appropriations from federal or state governments, and government or philanthropic grants and contracts.

Practice tip: All too often, elected officials pat themselves on the back for caring so much about children, the environment—whatever—knowing full well that without funding there is no implementation. Community champions need to be wise to the fact that a policy priority that only takes effect once funding is identified means that nothing happens until that funding is secured. Good intentions alone are meaningless without adequate funding.

4. **Ensure accountability**: Elected officials and government agency staff must be held accountable for the successful implementation of the law. A single top-level leader (e.g., governor, mayor, agency director, city manager, school superintendent) should be named in the law and held responsible for implementation. Such persons can delegate responsibility to others within their chain of command, but it is critical that a high-level government employee is listed in the public record as having ultimate responsibility.

   Practice tip: Assigning accountability to a specific leadership position means that community champions can become legislative watchdogs and know whom to target for action.

5. **Create timelines for action**: Accountable government leaders must be given timelines for action to guard against the risk of inactivity due to other pressing priorities. Strong laws typically require regulatory action within a certain number of months, quarterly or annual progress reports toward meeting policy goals, and other types of publicly available and regular feedback so both the legislature and the community champions can ensure the intent of the law is being met. Regular progress reports can become the basis for evaluation and continuous advocacy. (See #7)

   Practice tip: Progress reports also help flag any unintended consequences of implementing a law or policy. Future advocacy efforts can be identified via a virtuous cycle of implementation, reporting, evaluation, and action.

6. **Enforce the law**: Laws need both meaningful and equitable enforcement mechanisms to make sure their intent is carried forth in a manner that builds community strength and resiliency. Meaningful enforcement imposes appropriate sanctions on the appropriate wrongdoing. Most government agencies responsible for implementation of a law will start enforcement actions with stakeholder education and engagement, hoping never to progress to more onerous mechanisms like fines or penalties. But even when fines or penalties are needed, such action must be commensurate with known effectiveness and with equity goals in mind. For example, a retail permit to sell alcohol or tobacco can be revoked if owners of liquor or tobacco stores profit by selling alcohol or tobacco to minors, as no business has a right to profit by harming children. Yet the wrongdoings of underaged youth who illegally obtain alcohol or tobacco are best addressed by educational interventions or community service requirements that adhere to restorative justice principles at the core of equitable enforcement. Restorative justice includes strategies such as community dispute resolution processes or community service obligations that account for wrongdoing but also leave open the possibility for community healing and the reintegration of the wrongdoer into the community.

<u>Practice tip</u>: Equitable enforcement is a new area of public health practice. Community champions should stay abreast of the literature suggesting best practices in this area. For example, see Equitable Enforcement to Achieve Health Equity from Change-Lab Solutions.[3]

7. **Evaluate results**: Strong laws will have evaluation mechanisms embedded in the legislative text or in regulations to require monitoring of the policy's impact over time both to determine effectiveness and to identify unanticipated adverse outcomes that can be rectified in an amended law. Public reporting at designated intervals as discussed above provides opportunities for evaluation and continued advocacy. Other evaluation mechanisms include requiring public-facing recordkeeping that provides real-time data to community champions. For example, in many communities, the results of housing, food safety, workplace, or environmental health and safety inspections, and even police use-of-force incidents, are required to be posted on online and open-access portals. Such data transparency can fuel and support continuous advocacy efforts.

   <u>Practice tip</u>: To have maximum impact on equity goals, advocates need to stay involved in a legislative process through the development of implementing regulations.

8. **Avoid inequitable preemption**: The law is dynamic, and planning for the long-term should inform every step of the advocacy process to protect against unintended consequences and to ensure that innovations keep pace with science and practice. It is imperative that advocates develop a sophisticated understanding about the risks (and sometimes benefits) of federal and state preemption.[4]

   <u>Practice tip</u>: Community champions need to be smart about preemption. A community-organizing strategy must account for last-minute attempts at preemption by industry groups that could negatively affect health equity goals for many years to come. Careful analysis of specific situations to fully explore the pros and cons of preemption is also imperative for securing health equity. For more information, see the excellent resources on this subject at ChangeLab Solutions.[5]

The guidelines for practice outlined in this chapter are provided to inform community champions about how to most effectively leverage laws and policies to redress health inequities. As we seek to root out entrenched inequities, champions need sophisticated legal and policy strategies to maximize the limited windows of opportunity for effective health advocacy.

REFERENCES

1. Lezine D, Reed G. Political will: a bridge between public health knowledge and action. *Am J Public Health*. 2007;97(11):2010–13.

2. Mays GP, Mamaril CB, Timsina LR. Preventable death rates fell where communities expanded population health activities through multisector networks. *Health Aff (Millwood)*. 2016;35(11):2005–13.

3. Equitable Enforcement to Achieve Health Equity. ChangeLab Solutions. 2020. Available at: https://www.changelabsolutions.org/product/equitable-enforcement-achieve-health-equity. Accessed September 29, 2020.

4. Carr D, Adler S, Winig BD, Montez JK. Equity first: conceptualizing a normative framework to assess the role of preemption in public health. *Milbank Q*. 2020;98(1):131-49.

5. Consequences of Preemption for Public Health Equity. ChangeLab Solutions. 2020. Available at: https://www.changelabsolutions.org/sites/default/files/2020-08/Consequences_of_Preemption_FINAL_Accessible_20200710.pdf. Accessed September 30, 2020.

VI

CASE STUDIES IN COURAGE: POLICY APPROACHES TO THE SOCIAL DETERMINANTS OF HEALTH

Gun Safety in America: From Tragedy to Transformation

Dannel P. Malloy, JD

Every mile of America has been touched by the plague of gun violence. I know that all too well. On December 14, 2012, during my first year as the 88th governor of Connecticut, 26 lives were tragically lost—including 20 children between six and seven years old—in a horrific mass shooting at Sandy Hook Elementary School in Newtown, Connecticut.

Over a series of days, I and so many others—school leaders, state agencies, the state police, and other members of my administration—worked to help grieving families, entire communities, the state, and the nation come to grips with the tragedy that had occurred.

A member of the press asked me at the time, "Will there be change?" My response then was an unequivocal yes, because without meaningful change gun violence of a similar nature was certain to visit other towns, other cities, other homes. Unfortunately, that has proven to be the case.

Buoyed by unprecedented waves of activism from students, parents, and other grass-roots supporters of gun laws, state policymakers came together in Connecticut to pass some of the smartest, toughest gun safety laws in the country. But they were not without opposition.

PASSING GUN SAFETY LEGISLATION IN CONNECTICUT

When I saw how slowly things were moving both nationally and with the state legislature, I understood that as governor I had the ability to lay out specific, common-sense legislation at a time when others were mired in debate. This is the power of the executive branch, and I believed I owed it to the people of Connecticut, particularly to the deceased and the families of those who were deceased, to use that power fully as we struggled to recover from this horrendous act.

From the start, I decided that I was not going to kowtow to anyone, avoid difficult questions, or permit the status quo to continue. The families who lost loved ones deserved better. To put pressure on legislators to act, I went out across the state to champion the principles I felt so strongly about.

Mindful that many of those audiences would have gun proponents or anti-gun regulators present in great numbers, I was nevertheless willing to schedule the gatherings. I believed that somebody had to demonstrate that you could stand up to the detractors, answer their questions head-on, and not be bullied into giving up.

Before we held town halls, my team and I laid out what we wanted the legislation to look like. We decided to fight for our principles, including universal background checks and a ban on all military-style assault weapons and large-capacity magazines. We also debated important nuances within those stances, such as having a grandfather clause that allowed people to keep the large-capacity magazines they already had and only to ban their sale going forward. Though our debates were serious, and though there were detractors and complainers who wanted us to leave out these requirements, in the end we stayed true to our values and fought for everything.

The co-chairman of the state guns subcommittee, a Republican, argued, "We believe it's not the gun that kills the person. It's the person that actually kills the person. That sounds kind of cold, but that's the way it is,"[1] as if somehow guns are self-firing. There also was the issue of timing. Connecticut Republicans delayed action, even though New York, Colorado, and Maryland passed gun legislation after Sandy Hook. And then there was the National Rifle Association (NRA), which made robocalls around Newtown and bused crowds of gun-rights activists to the state capitol, all to fight what we believed was right.

We knew too that a state was only as strong as its neighbors' gun laws, for even in states and municipalities with strict gun safety laws, illegal guns are highly accessible and ever-present if there are weaker laws in adjacent states. Strong national legislation would have been far superior to individual states taking action, but if Congress wasn't going to act, Connecticut had to do something—we couldn't stand still in the wake of what we'd been through. That was why, despite lacking a bipartisan consensus for action in the state legislature, I knew that I would have to lead the charge to get the kind of result that the people of Connecticut deserved.

The final plan, proposed on February 21, 2013, included an expansion of the state's assault weapons ban and universal background checks, among other measures, while preserving citizens' Second Amendment rights. On April 3, 2013, the House passed what is now known as Public Act 13-3, *An Act Concerning Gun Violence and Children's Safety*, with a bipartisan vote of 105–44. The Senate approved the bill in a similar bipartisan fashion, 26–10, and the bill became law on April 4, 2013.

The day I signed the bill, Nicole Hockley, who lost her son Dylan to the Sandy Hook shooting, said, "We want Newtown to be known not for tragedy but for transformation." I hope that we are getting to that place, and that the passage of legislation was a major step in that process.[2]

GUN VIOLENCE IS ABOUT MORE THAN MASS SHOOTINGS

Mass shootings like Sandy Hook get the most attention, which is not surprising. But as I reflect on my time as governor, I know there were many other gun safety issues at stake that had less visibility.

Gun violence has been a persistent problem in many of our cities for decades. The simple fact is that more than two-thirds of homicides with firearms in Connecticut occur in the context of group- or gang-involved urban violence or domestic violence. The latter concern is why I called for passage of Public Act 16-3469, which prohibited the possession of firearms and ammunition, pending a court hearing, for persons subject to a temporary restraining order stemming from domestic violence. The act closed a dangerous loophole in the law pertaining to a time when victims are at their most vulnerable.

It was imperative that we looked at gun violence as a whole. In this country in 2019, nearly 40,000 Americans were killed by guns—almost 109 people each day. Of that, 60% (23,941) died by suicide.[3] While Connecticut's comprehensive gun safety legislation made our communities, schools, and places of business safer, it could not fully eliminate gun violence.

I believed then, as I do now, that state and federal leaders could solve these challenges with a firm determination to do so. Ninety-seven percent of Americans believe in universal background checks. As governor, I called out the NRA and Washington politicians beholden to it as being a relatively small number of people who had a stranglehold on maintaining the status quo of bad public policy on gun violence.[4] Resolute leaders must continue the fight; efforts at all levels must continue to change this.

THE RELATIONSHIP BETWEEN GUN REFORM AND OTHER KEY SOCIAL REFORMS

My mother, a public health professional and school nurse, told me every day that I had an obligation to leave the world a better place for my having lived in it. That's why I was committed to treating youth trauma as a means of proactively reducing violence.

We knew that children who witness the abuse of a parent or loved one are as badly impacted as the person who is abused. Yet proactive interventions were not required, nor were they easy to come by. The only way to change the outcome for a child who has grown up in that type of traumatic relationship is to treat the underlying problem along with any other trauma. If children are dying in someone's neighborhood, other children are affected, too. All of those underlying traumas lead to behaviors—including potential gun violence—that harm the individual, their communities, and society as a whole.

What I learned as governor was that gun safety legislation, though critically important, can be just one element of a larger approach to making ourselves safer. When we talk about guns, we have to talk about what happens before a person purchases a gun and commits a crime. What can we change to keep them from reaching that point?

On the public health side, it's not just gun control and it's not just preventing violence. We must also prepare our society to be ready for good health. Criminal justice reform, gun reform, health care access, education, and housing are all interrelated, and if all policy leaders saw it this way, we would be more likely to have substantially safer, healthier, better-educated, and better-housed communities.

The interrelated nature of these initiatives drove me, as governor, to concentrate on criminal justice reform, and I visited our state's prisons more than 20 times over the course of my two terms. In America, we send so many young people to jail—a place where they're more likely to learn more criminal behavior than anything else. We faced that issue head-on in Connecticut, and I'm proud to say we cut our youth incarceration rate by 66%.

Ninety-five percent of people who go to prison are going to come home from prison. Health care, mental health, job training, education, housing, employment, and faith-based opportunities are all important pieces of a successful reentry plan, without which many returning citizens struggle to successfully rejoin their communities and face the risk of recidivism.

When I left office, Connecticut had less than 13,000 people in jail, the lowest number in 25 years, which was down from 18,000 at the time I became governor. Crime is at a 50-year low—the largest decline in violent crime and the largest decline in a youthful population—and projections suggest that Connecticut could be the first state to halve its prison population and still have the lowest crime in 50 years.

CONCLUSION

As governor, I knew the people of Connecticut wanted to feel safe, and we felt the need for our children to be safe ever more acutely—a point Sandy Hook's tragedy so sadly brought home to us. When I left office, I remained convinced that we could not feel fully secure when 40% of guns change hands without a background check and when guns in homes are correlated with an increase in the overall youth suicide rate.[5] I think the best thing we can do is keep asking the hard questions about how we can come together to solve those problems with meaningful public policy, and I encourage all people—especially those holding public office—to use their voices and energy in support of smart, commonsense gun reform.

REFERENCES

1. Applebome P. 2 Conflicting legislative agendas arise from gun safety task force in Connecticut. *New York Times*. March 5, 2013. Available at: https://www.nytimes.com/2013/03/06/nyregion/2-conflicting-agendas-arise-from-gun-safety-task-force-in-connecticut.html. Accessed April 6, 2020.

2. Bacon J, Stanglin D. Conn governor signs USA's toughest gun law. *USA Today*. April 4, 2013. Available at: https://www.usatoday.com/story/news/nation/2013/04/04/connecticut-gun-control/2052235. Accessed April 6, 2020.

3. Educational Fund to Stop Gun Violence. A public health crisis decades in the making: a review of 2019 CDC gun mortality data. February 2021. Available at: https://efsgv.org/wp-content/uploads/2019CDCdata.pdf. Accessed March 15, 2021.

4. Martin M. Conn governor defends likening the NRA to 'a terrorist organization'. NPR. March 10, 2018. Available at: https://www.npr.org/2018/03/10/592282517/conn-governor-defends-likening-the-nra-to-a-terrorist-organization. Accessed April 6, 2020.

5. Jacobs T. Household guns linked to youth suicides. *Pacific Standard*. January 17, 2019. Available at: https://psmag.com/social-justice/household-guns-linked-to-youth-suicides. Accessed April 6, 2020.

19

Housing: A Case Study in Rental Inspection Policy in Kansas City, Missouri

Rex Archer, MD, MPH and Stacie Duitsman, MPH

INTRODUCTION

There is a tap on my office door. I glance down at my calendar and double-check my schedule—I am not expecting anyone. Curiosity gets the best of me, and I make my way to the door. I open it to find one of the health department's nurses, specifically a public health nurse who works in our Childhood Lead Poisoning Prevention Program. As we get settled, she begins to tell me about a risk assessment inspection she conducted earlier in the day. The pictures she has brought with her illustrate the rental home a family is staying in. I scan images of disrepair and despair. As I look at one picture, she tells me that a three-year-old toddler is staying in this room. From the picture, you can tell the parents are trying to do their best, but there is a hole in the floor "large enough for even you, the department director, to fall through," she says.

I knew we had a problem, but in that moment I all but smacked myself in the head and then proclaimed it was time to do something. Complaints were rolling in by the dozens, but there were no ordinances in place to establish minimum health and safety standards on rental properties in Kansas City. Over 21 years ago, before I came to be "head coach" of the Kansas City Health Department, there had been an attempt to regulate rental housing. That attempt failed miserably. At the time, there wasn't a group advocating for tenants' rights or even department partners putting their efforts toward healthy, safe rental housing.

Learning from history and that failed effort, I knew we would face challenges in bringing this back to the table. I gathered a passionate team of professionals within our department and began to brainstorm ways to tackle this problem that encompasses so much more than just rental housing—it influences everything from emergency room visits and asthma attacks and hospitalizations to school and job attendance and feelings of self-worth, to mention just a few. In Kansas City, we tried to wrap our heads around the data. It appeared that more than 24,000 of our residents (1 in 20) were living in substandard rental housing. Aiming for all city residents to have access to safe, stable, and affordable housing was a difficult challenge that would require a multifaceted policy response.

We knew where to start. The health department had created strategic partnerships with advocacy grassroots organizations throughout the years to take on issues like predatory lending, raising the minimum wage, and rehabilitation of jailed individuals back into the workforce, but none of these groups had protecting renters from unhealthy rental properties on their advocacy agenda. We needed to approach these partners and enlist them in building a social movement.

GATHERING CHAMPIONS FOR THE HEALTHY HOMES RENTAL INSPECTION PROGRAM

Luck is where "preparation meets opportunity." We were selected to participate in a five-city cohort with the National League of Cities to address health and housing. This cohort provided us the opportunity to create partnerships with local public health agencies throughout the country that also were tackling health and housing through rental inspection programs, forming an essential support group of subject matter experts that became crucial over the next three years.

In December 2015, the Kansas City team traveled to Dallas, Texas, with Mayor Sly James and Mayor Pro Tem Scott Wagner. This first cohort meeting set the stage for the research needed to make a rental housing program that addressed health and safety a reality in Kansas City.

It would be nice to say that opposition was minimal, because you wouldn't think there would be objection to providing safe and healthy living conditions for everyone. Wrong. Opposition to the Healthy Homes Rental Inspection Program was substantial. Large real estate organizations, small family-owned rental property owners, and corporate management groups were quick to show their disapproval for "another piece of legislation to control business owners." They thought the new ordinance wouldn't target slum landlords and would penalize only the good ones through permit and reinspection fees.

Having the mayor pro tem as our "product champion," providing unwavering support to finding a solution that would benefit tenants and landlords, was invaluable. He scheduled biweekly meetings with these interests to find a workable solution. Even when unable to do so, the health department and mayor pro tem decided to move forward. We drafted a proposed ordinance—not the all-encompassing one the city needed, but one that could start to address rental housing. Simultaneously, we took our data to community organizations that on a local level had begun to address housing and other social/political influencers of health. This would end up being the checkmate move, as these community organizations became a crucial part in moving the rental housing program forward.

In the fall of 2017, we introduced the ordinance proposal to the city council's housing committee. The department presented the ordinance, the years of research data, and expected outcomes of the measure. What we didn't do at that time was turn out the numbers. While there were supporters present, the opposition outnumbered us to speak their stance on the ordinance and the unintended consequences it would have on them as landlords. The proposal was held until the committee's next session.

Two weeks later, we went back to present before the housing committee. This time, tenants had heard of the ordinance and showed up to tell their stories. The proposal gained additional attention from local news media in attendance. This was a controversial ordinance, and many weren't sure it would solve the housing crisis that Kansas City was facing. Would it decrease the number of available rental units? Would there be a spike in affordable housing? Would it put people on the streets? These uncertainties divided the city council and resulted in the proposal being held indefinitely.

By having an elected official as one of the biggest supporters of establishing housing standards in Kansas City, we weren't out of options. The City of Kansas City government offers the community the ability to create an initiative petition and have issues placed on the ballot without approval of the city council. This became the Hail Mary option. Our community partners took matters into their own hands, and five such groups collected more than 2,000 signatures in the form of a petition to place the Healthy Homes Rental Inspection Program ordinance on the ballot.

On August 7, 2018, despite widespread opposition from landlords and financial backing to lobby against it, the initiative passed with a 57% majority. That night, I knew this could be the start of further addressing the life expectancy gap among zip codes in Kansas City.

The ordinance went live 30 days later, and at the end of the first year the Healthy Homes Rental Inspection Program had responded to more than 1,400 complaints ranging from pests and ventilation/mold issues to water/wastewater, structural, and life safety violations. While Healthy Homes Rental Inspection is still in its infancy, it shows great promise for long-lasting success. At the one-year mark, impressed with the success of the program, the city council unanimously changed the ordinance to include HUD and Housing Authority properties. This was a boon, giving the program the ability to inspect an additional 20,000 rental properties in the city. We look forward to the day when a program evaluation can be conducted to assess what difference it has made in all aspects of health, including asthma hospitalizations, violence, and even life expectancy.

CONCLUSION

Our public health approach has grown out of General Colin Powell's 40-70 rule:

Use the formula P = 40 to 70, in which P stands for the probability of success and the numbers indicate the percentage of information acquired. Once the information is in the 40 to 70 range, go with your gut. Don't take action if you have only enough information to give you less than a 40% chance of being right, but don't wait until you have enough facts to be 100% sure, because by then it is almost always too late. Today, excessive delays in the name of information-gathering breeds "analysis paralysis." Procrastination in the name of reducing risk actually increases risk.[1]

In government (outside of the military), the norm tends to be P = 90% to 100%. To save lives, entrepreneurial health departments attempt to strike a balance between these two approaches in the range of P = 55% to 85%.

There still is some unknown that most local governments face when it comes to state preemption, but we are hopeful the Missouri legislature will acknowledge the positive impact this ordinance has had on housing here in Kansas City.

REFERENCES

1. Powell C. A leadership primer. Homeland Security Digital Library. 2006. Available at: https://www.hsdl.org/?abstract&did=467329. Accessed June 6, 2020.

20

Early Education: Why Quality Pre-K Is Worth the Investment

Ellen Frede, PhD and W. Steven Barnett, PhD

INTRODUCTION

Most of the achievement gap that concerns America—between the rich and everyone else, between White people and people of color—is generated before children ever walk through the kindergarten door. The roots of educational, economic, social, and health disparities are to be found in the earliest years of life, and these disparities can be reduced through participation in high-quality pre-K.[1] To address these gaps, elected officials in some of the nation's largest cities and in 44 states in all regions of the country have enacted a burst of new pre-K education policies. The funding mechanisms and specific pre-K policies are as varied as the locales in which they were started, but all were motivated by common concerns—the importance of early learning for school readiness and lifelong development, children's disparate skills at kindergarten entry, concern about the inequality of access to pre-K, and the high cost of good pre-K programs. City and state governments have an important role to play in establishing publicly funded pre-K and providing adequate funding to promote quality and access.

The support of local and state policymakers is built on decades of multidisciplinary research on the benefits of participation in high-quality pre-K. These immediate and lifelong benefits go beyond education to include social and economic well-being and can result in improvements in mental and physical health.[2] Children who attend pre-K are more likely to access health care of all kinds and receive better nutrition.[1] In programs that target interventions to parents, reductions have been found in child abuse and neglect. Improvements in participants' self-regulation and cognitive abilities lead to better problem-solving skills and reduce risky behaviors later. Adults who attended pre-K have improved health behaviors and enjoy better health. All of these benefits lead to savings to participants and society in health care and other costs.[1]

CURRENT CONTEXT FOR PRE-K EDUCATION

Historically, few children enrolled in preschool programs, but that began to change several decades ago.[3] Today, most four-year-old children spend time in a classroom before they enter kindergarten. However, access remains highly unequal, with children of color and from low-income families having the least access to good preschool programs, and improvement has been painfully slow. Currently, less than 25% of four-year-olds and a very small percentage of three-year-olds have access to high-quality pre-K—the kind of pre-K that leads to lasting benefits. At our current rate of growth in pre-K provision, it will take 150 years to reach 75% enrollment, and much of that preschool provision will not meet the policy benchmarks necessary to support quality.[3]

The wide range of benefits for children, families, and communities are found only when programs are of high quality.[4] This is true regardless of the name under which that preschool education program is offered: pre-K, Head Start, child care, or nursery school. Even within a statewide universal pre-K program, quality can vary systemically, with disadvantaged children receiving lower quality pre-K education. For all these reasons it is imperative for cities and states to invest in raising quality as well as expanding the number of places available.

The chain of pre-K benefits from cradle to career and beyond generates economic benefits far exceeding cost, giving public investments in good pre-K a high rate of return.[5] Paradoxically, limiting eligibility to children in poverty in an attempt to raise rates of economic return by focusing on those who benefit most can reduce the economic payoff. Programs that serve all children are most likely to fully enroll, and produce large gains for, the most disadvantaged while still yielding benefits for other children. However, obtaining these benefits depends critically on the quality of the program offered. Despite their great potential, publicly funded pre-K programs do not always produce the kinds of results that generate a positive economic return. Several large public preschool initiatives in the United States and abroad have been found to yield little in the way of long-term gains.

WHAT IS QUALITY?

Science helps to define what constitutes good pre-K education.[2,4,5] Fundamentally, pre-K quality is about relationships. These include the relationships between teachers and children, between children and their peers, and between children and educational materials and toys. Good teachers are intentional, engaging, responsive, and caring. They help children learn to regulate their own emotions and behavior, plan and take responsibility, work well with others, problem solve, and acquire the knowledge and skills that are the foundations for later academic success as well as curiosity and a love of learning. High-quality pre-K offers more than good teaching.[5] Good programs also meet children's nutritional needs; screen for, identify, and address developmental delays and disabilities, including vision and hearing impairment; and engage with parents as partners in supporting their children's learning and development. Pre-K can improve home as well as out-of-home experiences by offering parenting education and referrals to social, health, and other services a child and family may need.

Pre-K quality, as described here, typically is referred to by early childhood experts as "process quality."[3] The field also recognizes "structural quality," which refers to the features of program design that facilitate process quality. Structural features that have received the most attention include teacher qualifications, teacher training, class size, and teacher-student ratio. Structural quality can be said to be a necessary but not sufficient basis for process quality.

PROMOTING POLICIES FOR HIGH QUALITY AND ACCESS

Despite all the guidance science offers, convincing policymakers to provide funding to increase access to high-quality pre-K is difficult. Across the pre-K effectiveness research, there are two basic failures in pre-K policy and practice. The first is failure to design a pre-K program that encompasses all of the features of the effective programs. For example, only two states offer the low teacher-to-child ratio seen in the most effective programs, and only four states require that teachers have an early childhood education (ECE) teaching license and be paid on par with K–12 teachers.[3] The second is failure to implement the program as designed. Both failures frequently result from inadequate funding, but underlying that is often a lack of appreciation for what is required for a high-quality program. Perhaps least understood is that substantial funding is required to support implementation of quality through direct technical assistance to programs and professional development for teaching staff, monitoring, and continuous improvement systems.

In 2002, to spur policymakers and enhance public will, the National Institute for Early Education Research (NIEER) began producing an annual *State of Preschool Yearbook* that rates state pre-K programs on access, funding, and 10 benchmarks for quality policy that are described in Table 20-1.[3] To determine the quality policy standards, NIEER employed the same process that businesses commonly use to design a quality production system, "benchmarking" against industry leaders, which in this case are the model programs and exemplars that have shown effectiveness. These benchmarks were verified in the much broader scientific literature. Recently, this same approach has been used to rate pre-K in large cities as part of the CityHealth initiative to award medals to cities that promote research-based health policies.

No single policy is a silver bullet for high quality. Some policies may be more important than others, but success is contingent on designing a coherent set of policies that is strongly supported and implemented as a system. As in every other policy area, everything may not work out as planned, and it is critical that programs have ongoing evaluation as part of their continuous improvement process as a basis for course corrections to

Table 20-1. NIEER Pre-K Quality Policy Benchmarks

Policy Benchmark	Description	Why It Matters
Learning goals	Comprehensive early learning and development standards to guide teaching and assessment	Programs need clear and appropriate goals explaining what children are expected to know and be able to do.
Curriculum supports	Guidance for choosing and using content-rich curriculum	Programs should use curricula that integrate learning in language, literacy, mathematics, science, and social-emotional development.
Teacher education level	Lead teachers required to have a bachelor's degree	Teachers with higher education levels generally provide higher-quality learning environments for children.
Teacher specialized training	Lead teacher has specialized training for teaching pre-K	Teachers need to understand how to teach in ways that are consistent with a child's learning and development.
Assistant teacher education	Assistant teacher has a formalized entry-level credential such as the Child Development Associate	All members of a teaching team influence classroom quality, so assistants should hold at least an entry-level qualification for teaching young children.
Professional development	Ongoing training for teachers and assistant teachers	Professional learning, including coaching and other classroom support, produces high-quality learning experiences for children.
Maximum class size	Maximum number of children per classroom is 20	Effective pre-K programs have small classes, enabling teachers to understand and address each child's interests, needs, and capabilities.
Teacher-child ratio	Ratio of teachers to children is 1:10 or better	Working with small groups of children allows teachers to offer more individualized attention, which results in better outcomes.
Health screening and referral	Screenings for vision, hearing, health, and developmental concerns, along with referrals to needed services	Screening for health and development issues provides children with the help they need and often prevents later costly services.
Continuous quality improvement system	System to assess program quality used to guide improvement	Using data to inform program improvement helps educators provide the high-quality early learning opportunities children need.

Source: Based on Friedman-Krauss.[3]

policy and policy implementation. Illuminating state and local pre-K policies has proved to be an effective method of instigating improvements. In 2002, when the first *State of Preschool Yearbook* was conducted, no states met all 10 NIEER benchmarks, and most met fewer than half. In the latest yearbook, three states now meet all 10 of the benchmarks and only 12 programs meet fewer than half. Additionally, enrollment in state-funded pre-K alone has more than doubled for four-year-olds from 14% to 33% of total population. Highlighting data on policy trends can be a powerful motivator to elected and appointed officials for improving program requirements.

City and state elected and appointed officials regularly request technical assistance from NIEER to help them meet the benchmarks and scale their pre-K program. To augment and refine the benefits of publishing states' and cities' progress toward increased access in high-quality pre-K, NIEER and others have partnered with state and local ECE leadership to provide technical assistance and facilitate networking. This motivation to "be the best" is not the same as wanting to be better than others, and in our work with state and city leaders we find that these leaders embrace and seek collaboration and learning communities as a powerful change mechanism. Since the publication of the first yearbook, NIEER has supported the professional membership organization of ECE specialists in state government to meet and learn from each other. Recently, a network of city pre-K leads was piloted, and these local leaders are eager to continue and expand their network. Facilitators and members in both networks share effective solutions to the problems of weak policies that do not meet the designs of the models, policy implementation failure, and lack of funding. Technical assistance has included leadership development, data gathering and analysis, and tools for understanding system challenges. For example, to ensure that the resources match the design demands, states have used the Cost of Preschool Program Quality Calculator, which requires stakeholders to clearly define the components of their pre-K policy. The tool then calculates the full cost of implementing the proposed policy components centrally focused on the 10 NIEER yearbook benchmarks. Stakeholders use this to develop a strategic plan to adequately fund and implement a high-quality pre-K program, understanding the consequences of any trade-offs. The city pre-K network is developing a self-assessment framework to help city stakeholders evaluate their policies and plan for improvements toward meeting all the NIEER yearbook benchmarks as well as a number of other critical components for effective pre-K.

The 10 benchmarks are not the only policies that matter. Funding must be adequate to implement these policies well. For example, if teacher compensation remains at low levels, increasing staff qualifications requirements could make recruiting and retaining strong teachers even more difficult. Duration is important, with children who start at age three benefiting more than those who begin at age four, and offering at least full-school-day programs is more likely to result in benefits for children and better meet the needs of working parents. Additionally, every year of a child's life is important for learning and development, so policymakers should attend as well to what comes before and what comes after pre-K. Lasting benefits from pre-K may be squandered if kindergarten and the early grades are not aligned with children's experiences and capabilities coming out of pre-K.

Wide and deep bipartisan support for pre-K is leading to more funding and a strong focus on implementing effective programs. Increasingly, the importance of the early years from conception to age eight is being embraced by this same group of supporters with a clear understanding that the social determinants of health are intertwined with the social determinants of educational attainment, especially in the early years. With this heightened understanding, young children's path to health and well-being is more likely a reality.

REFERENCES

1. Friedman-Krauss A, Barnett WS. Early childhood education: pathways to better health. The National Institute for Early Education Research. April, 2013. Available at: http://nieer.org/wp-content/uploads/2016/08/health20brief.pdf. Accessed February 16, 2020.

2. Phillips DA, Lipsey MW, Dodge KA, et al. Puzzling it out: the current state of scientific knowledge on pre-kindergarten effects, a consensus statement. Washington, DC: Brookings Institute. April 17, 2017. Available at: https://www.brookings.edu/wp-content/uploads/2017/04/consensus-statement_final.pdf. Accessed February 16, 2020.

3. Friedman-Krauss AH, Barnett WS, Garver KA, et al. The state of preschool 2018: state preschool yearbook. The National Institute for Early Education Research. April 2019. Available at: http://nieer.org/wp-content/uploads/2019/05/YB2018_Executive-SummaryR.pdf. Accessed February 16, 2020.

4. Ramon I, Chattopadhyay SK, Hahn R, et al. Early childhood education to promote health equity: a community guide economic review. January/February 2016. Available at: https://www.thecommunityguide.org/sites/default/files/publications/he-jphmp-ecrev-early-childhood-education.pdf. Accessed February 16, 2020.

5. Shonkoff JP, Phillips DA, editors. *From neurons to neighborhoods: the science of early childhood development*. Washington, DC: National Academy Press; 2000.

21

Tobacco Control: Going Smoke-Free Deep in Tobacco Country

Karen Remley, MD, MBA, MPH

Passing laws that are based on the public health principle of protecting the community over the rights of an individual are always a delicate balance of science, compromise, and timing. The right to smoke is one of these issues that has been fought over in every state-house across the country. Increasing both tobacco taxes and the legal age to purchase tobacco, as well as banning smoking in public places such as restaurants, are proven policies that significantly and positively impact the health of communities. Below is the story of how successful legislation to ban smoking in restaurants required science, compromise, timing, and some luck.

The story of tobacco and the Commonwealth of Virginia begins more than 400 years ago.[1] After observing that tobacco was successfully cultivated by Native Americans, John Rolfe brought milder Spanish seeds to the Commonwealth in 1611 and began growing tobacco as a cash crop to be sent back to England for great profit. Tobacco was instrumental to the growth and success of the colony, an economy that relied on slave labor and indentured servitude to survive and thrive; tobacco farming, processing, inspecting, and shipping drove development of communities and ports dependent on this crop. The nascent General Assembly began regulating the propagation, sale, establishment of ports, and taxing of tobacco beginning in 1632 by limiting the number of plants for each plantation to 1,500. Ever since, countless laws and regulations have been promulgated and enforced in Virginia as tobacco has remained instrumental in and interwoven with the state's history. Even today, as you enter the Richmond area, the Altria building complex reminds us that one of the largest producers of cigarettes in the world is headquartered in Virginia's capital city. Upon touring the Thomas Jefferson–designed Capitol building, visitors learn that the plaster leaves decorating the edifice and encircling the General Assembly rooms might represent tobacco. The roots of both the plant and its impact on Virginia politics run deep. Because of this legacy, efforts to regulate and tax tobacco in Virginia have been slow and lagged behind many other states.

Governor Tim Kaine was elected in 2005 as a moderate Democrat with a goal of working across the aisle and solving complex problems in a uniquely Virginian way. He understood the public health effects of smoking and secondhand smoke. He also knew that passing a smoking ban would require careful lawmaking in light of Virginia's history. Governor Kaine quickly implemented a smoking ban in all state buildings through an executive order to help reduce the impact of smoking and secondhand smoke on state employees. A pragmatist, he allowed the Department of Corrections and Department of Behavioral Health more leeway in developing and easing into their plans. Simultaneously, some Virginia communities began to implement smoking bans in local government buildings, and at least one local government was considering a ban in restaurants. To test the political waters, in 2007 Governor Kaine added a smoking ban in restaurants to a bill sponsored by Morgan Griffith. Griffith's original bill required that signs be displayed in restaurants to designate where smoking was allowed but eliminated the requirement for restaurants to maintain a nonsmoking section. While Governor Kaine's smoking ban was ultimately defeated, as anticipated, he was pleasantly surprised that the vote had a smaller margin than he had expected. Throughout the Commonwealth, constituents were letting their elected officials know they were ready for action on this important public health issue.

The year 2008 brought not only President Obama but also Ralph Northam, a new Democratic Virginia senator who was a pediatric neurologist. Kaine asked Northam to carry the bill to ban smoking in restaurants, believing that having a legislative champion who was a pediatric physician would provide additional gravitas and credibility. The Virginia Senate had a Democratic majority at the time, but the House of Delegates was controlled by Republicans. A House subcommittee opted to kill the bill, perhaps worried that it might pass if it got to the floor. Kaine and Northam, ready to play the long game for public health, prepared to try again in the next legislative session the following year. Meanwhile, that fall the Virginia Department of Health began including the smoking status of each restaurant listed on its website among other health information. This effort continued to build awareness with restaurants and with the public of the desire to protect people from dangerous secondhand smoke.

In 2007, a statewide poll had shown that over 70% of Virginians were in favor of a smoking ban in restaurants. Armed with this demonstration of broad constituent support, Kaine continued to pursue the ban. The 2008 recession resulted in decreased revenues for the state, leaving a gap in the Medicaid budget. The federal government was preparing a federal stimulus package, and Kaine's administration was hopeful but not certain the stimulus would come through and fix the hole in the budget. Kaine and his chief counsel, Mark Rubin, decided to put forth two bills related to smoking in 2009. The first bill increased the cigarette tax to fund Medicaid and the second brought back Northam's smoking in restaurants ban for another bite at the apple. This one-two approach was strategic, as moderate Republicans did not want to support additional taxes; the second bill seemed more favorable in comparison, especially considering that constituents and local governments were already behind this move. As expected, advocates, public health officials, and clinicians lined up to testify, but a new group joined their ranks: the restaurant workers who were exposed to secondhand smoke through their jobs. Employees who had little control or choice over their working environment were being exposed to toxins—and looked at the issue from a different perspective than restaurant patrons, who could choose where they ate.

As the session progressed, the legislature began horse-trading around components of the second bill. After a series of conversations, collaborations, and concessions, the legislature and administration coalesced around several final amendments. This compromise exempted tobacco company cafeterias from the ban and allowed restaurants to build a defined smoking room if the room had separate ventilation and the restaurant had employees willing to work in that environment. The final bill also provided a delayed start date and required enforcement by the Virginia Department of Health (VDH). Ultimately, a number of Republican lawmakers sagely listened to their constituencies and joined in voting this important public health bill into law.

Beginning in the summer of 2007, two years before the bill passed, VDH brought together stakeholders to discuss the definition of restaurant and then presented that definition to the General Assembly's Joint Commission on Administrative Rules.[2] Bars in Virginia need to serve food in order to serve alcohol, so they too met the definition. As the bills moved forward, the VDH prepared for what might eventually be a requirement to regulate a ban through its restaurant inspection responsibilities. Once the ban was passed, stakeholders gathered at the VDH offices in the summer of 2009 to hammer out the regulations that would implement and enforce the ban and provide clarity and efficiency to restaurants and the public. Structural, functional, and signage responsibilities for restaurants were developed through collaboration with multiple agencies.[3] Borderline cases—like the question of whether farm stands that sell pies count as restaurants—and rule-making on how to design a separate smoking section were discussed and debated. Local government officials, restaurant owners, lobbyists, and advocates with a variety of perspectives all joined in these meetings.

That fall, in anticipation of the law taking effect December 1, extensive public awareness campaigns began. On November 19, National Smoke-Free Day, Karen Remley, the state's health commissioner, encouraged all Virginians to celebrate by going to their favorite smoke-free restaurant.[4] Postcards and placards that shared information about the date of implementation were developed for display on restaurant tables. On December 1, 2009, Kaine, Northam, and Remley traveled to those restaurants that bravely went smoke-free first, thanking them for their commitment to providing healthy environments for their employees and patrons and celebrating the successful culmination of this multiyear effort to bring smoke-free restaurants to Virginia (Figure 21-1)[4].

The story would be incomplete if we didn't look at what happened in the ensuing 10 years. Was the ban hard to implement? Were there many complaints or noncompliant restaurants? Before the ban, it was noted in restaurant inspections that over 30% of Virginia restaurants were smoke-free.

Are you ready to go smoke-free?

New legislation takes effect **Dec. 1, 2009**, to protect restaurant workers and patrons from the harmful effects of secondhand smoke. The Virginia Department of Health encourages restaurant owners and managers to visit our Web site, www.vdh.virginia.gov, for information on how your restaurant can go smoke-free and comply with the new law. Breathe easy, Virginia.

For assistance on specific questions, contact the Office of Environmental Health Services at (804) 864-7473 or e-mail Gary Hagy at Gary.Hagy@vdh.virginia.gov.

VDH VIRGINIA DEPARTMENT OF HEALTH
Protecting You and Your Environment

QUIT NOW VIRGINIA
Tobacco User Quitline • 1-800-QUIT-NOW

Source: Reprinted with permission from Virginia Department of Health.[4]

Figure 21-1. Breathe Easy, VA

There were a few complaints in the first year, a few arrests for smoking in a restaurant, and one lawsuit involving a hookah bar, which VDH won. When vaping e-cigarettes arrived, the state's attorney general, when asked, offered a formal opinion that the restaurant smoking ban was not applicable. But by that time, the restaurants, their patrons, and the general public had adjusted to smoke-free restaurants, and hence there were no significant changes. Only 0.7% of food facilities had made accommodations to allow smoking in their indoor areas, with an additional 1.6% setting up outdoor smoking areas (Table 21-1).

Table 21-1. Smoking Status for Permitted Food Establishments*

Food Facility Smoking Status	Count
Indoor	164
Outdoor smoking area	364
Smoke-free	21,275
Smoking in designated areas	340
TOTAL	**22,143**

Source: Bob Hicks, Deputy Commissioner Community Health, VDH, email communication on March 1, 2020.
*Permit types were Caterer, Convenience Store Food Service, Fast Food, Full Service Restaurant, or Grocery Store Food Service.

More than a decade later, this public health intervention is used as a teaching example for developing a multi-year and multi-stakeholder strategy to move other important public health policy initiatives through the General Assembly. A ban on texting while driving and an increase to the smoking age both followed similar playbooks. Imagine how many Virginians' lives have been improved by this public health intervention and its impact on ongoing policy interventions to improve health and well-being.

Acknowledgments: Tim Kaine, US Senator and former Governor of Virginia, made contributions to this chapter.

REFERENCES

1. Salmon EJ, Salmon J. Tobacco in colonial Virginia. Encyclopedia Virginia website. January 2013. Available at: http://www.EncyclopediaVirginia.org/Tobacco_in_Colonial_Virginia. Accessed June 15, 2020.

2. Joint Commission on Administrative Rules. Virginia Department of Health actions on smoking in restaurants. Division of Legislative Automated Systems website. Available at: http://services.dlas.virginia.gov/User_db/frmView.aspx?ViewId=1917&s=19. July 10, 2007. Accessed June 15, 2020.

3. Memorandum of agreement between the Virginia Department of Health, the Virginia Department of Housing and Community Development and the Virginia Department of Agriculture Consumer Services. Virginia Department of Health files. October 2009.

4. Virginia Department of Health. VDH commissioner asks Virginians to support the Commonwealth Breath Easy Challenge. Virginia Department of Health files. November 19, 2009.

22

Economic Security and Health:
Making the Case for Paid Sick Leave

Lili Farhang, MPH and Jonathan Heller, PhD

The COVID-19 pandemic has underscored an alarming gap in public policy: Tens of millions of people in the United States do not receive paid sick leave from their employers, yet many work in jobs that are essential to our collective health and well-being. And while some state and local governments enacted paid sick leave policies during the pandemic, nearly all were temporary. Further, the federal Families First Coronavirus Response Act[1] failed to protect more than 100 million workers, including those working for businesses with more than 500 or fewer than 50 employees.

Since the early days of the pandemic, the public health community encouraged people to stay home if they experienced signs of illness. But the lack of paid sick leave is a contraindication to this advice—the directive is much harder for workers without paid sick leave to follow, as they risk loss of jobs or income. Evidence shows this reality hampered the country's COVID-19 response and led to countless cases, outbreaks, and deaths.[2]

The connection between access to paid sick leave and health is not new. In 2008, Human Impact Partners (HIP) and the San Francisco Department of Public Health (SFDPH) partnered to conduct a Health Impact Assessment (HIA) of a proposed state-mandated paid sick leave policy. We found that paid sick days had numerous and expansive benefits for both individual and community health. At the time, San Francisco was the only jurisdiction in the country to have a paid sick leave law on the books. Since then, 14 states, Washington, DC, and over 20 other cities and counties have enacted paid sick leave laws. Yet, as we have seen with COVID-19, gaps in coverage remain widespread.

This brief case study examines paid sick days as an example of how public health practitioners can apply data and framing to make the case for an economic security issue. We share our story with the transparent intention of motivating the wider public health community to use its resources, evidence, and moral authority to take action on the social and economic determinants that drive health and equity.

THE FIRST PAID SICK DAYS HIA

In 2008, the California Work & Family Coalition approached HIP and SFDPH about conducting a HIA of the California Healthy Families, Healthy Workplaces Act.[3] The bill would have provided an hour of paid sick time for every 30 hours worked, affecting 5.4 million workers in the state who did not have paid sick leave protections. Simply put, the goal was to demonstrate the impact of paid sick leave to state policymakers who were debating the legislation.

We took a holistic approach in our assessment to demonstrate the far-reaching influence of paid sick leave legislation. We analyzed the choices available to workers—including restaurant, retail, child care, and nursing home workers—when they got sick and how those connected to a variety of health outcomes. We reviewed the existing literature and data about paid sick time, performed new analyses of existing data, and conducted focus groups with workers. We looked at the potential effects on individuals, families, and communities.

The assessment revealed health inequities resulting from the lack of paid sick leave. Overall, paid sick leave was inaccessible to those who needed it most. The impacts were deep:

- 79% of the lowest-earning workers and 70% of workers in the food service industry did not have paid sick leave and faced greater threats of lost wages, retaliation, and job loss compared with employees in higher-paid positions.
- Nearly half of workers who reported being in fair or poor health did not have paid sick leave, compared with one-quarter of workers who reported good or excellent health.
- Focus group participants described being forced to go to work despite being sick in order to make ends meet, though they knew they would get coworkers and customers sick.

The HIA predicted numerous positive impacts that paid sick leave policies would have for workers, families, and communities if enacted in California. We found the following:

- Provision of paid sick days would reduce seasonal flu, pandemic flu, foodborne illness transmission in restaurants, and communicable disease transmission in health and child care facilities.
- Workers would use primary health care more and emergency rooms less.
- Workers would not have the choice of going to work sick and staying home and not being able to pay rent or buy food.
- There were no downsides to paid sick leave policies, even from an economic perspective.

Importantly, other researchers subsequently confirmed and expanded on our findings:

- Workers without paid sick leave are three times more likely to delay or forgo needed care.[4]
- An estimated five million people contracted the H1N1 virus during the 2009 pandemic because of a lack of policies such as paid sick leave.[5]
- When employees are able to access paid sick days, there is a significant reduction in annual influenza infections.[5]

USING THE HIA FINDINGS TO SHIFT NARRATIVE AND POLICY

We released the HIA report, along with a more accessible report summary, to make our case to policymakers. We paired quantitative data and workers' stories to show how people and communities would be positively affected by the legislation, and we used our public health authority and voice to testify to these facts.

Through the legislative process and press conferences, we made it clear that whether you work in a restaurant or eat in one, work in a day care or have a child in one, or work in a nursing home or have a family member in one, workers' ability to access paid sick leave affects everyone's health. We were able to explain to policymakers that paid sick leave is not about "those workers" who come to work ill, but about all of us—our community as a whole.

The report and communications framing helped legislators make a personal connection to the cause and understand their own well-being in relation to paid sick leave policies. Ultimately, we helped shift the paid sick leave conversation from being solely about labor rights to being about our collective health and safety.

Despite this, the Healthy Workplace, Healthy Families Act of 2008 failed to pass.* Over the following years, HIP continued to support advocacy organizations in California and around the country to create similar state- and local-level HIAs on paid sick leave.[6] Our initial report and approach influenced campaigns across the country—many of which successfully enacted paid sick leave legislation—and changed the nature of the debate.

Six years after our initial study, California ultimately passed the Healthy Workplace, Healthy Families Act of 2014, guaranteeing that all workers accrue an hour of paid sick leave for every 30 hours worked. This time can be used by individual employees who are

---

*California was in the midst of a budget crisis and the legislation had a budget impact because it would require the state government to provide paid sick time to in-home health care workers, who were state contractors. The fiscal cost was perceived at the time to be too high.

managing or recovering from illness as well as to care for sick family members. In addition, it can be used by employees who are experiencing interpersonal violence, sexual assault, or stalking.

EXPANDING PUBLIC HEALTH'S ROLE IN ECONOMIC SECURITY

Alongside many others in public health, HIP has continued to connect a wide range of economic security issues to health, including minimum wage, wage theft, unpredictable work hours and schedules, and gig economy working conditions. This work continues to demonstrate that people's jobs, income, and working conditions are among the most important determinants of health.

Long before the public health and economic crises ushered in by COVID-19, people were already living on the economic edge. Indeed, 40% of Americans report that they would have difficulty covering a $400 emergency expense[7]—and their health is suffering as a result. As public health practitioners, we have long understood how economic security relates to health, and we have troves of data to connect the dots.

But public health practitioners need encouragement and an entry point to act on this knowledge. Our body of work on paid sick leave shows how we can bring multiple forms of data together, frame an issue from a health and equity perspective, and advocate—with those most impacted—for policy change to improve the health of those who need it most.

When we do this, we succeed on many fronts. Policymakers and the public better understand the connections between economic security and health. Public health practitioners use their voice and power to improve the social and economic conditions that drive health. And most important, people can live healthier lives with a greater sense of control and peace of mind for themselves and their loved ones.

REFERENCES

1. Families First Coronavirus Response Act: employer paid leave requirements. US Department of Labor. 2013. Available at: https://www.dol.gov/agencies/whd/pandemic/ffcra-employer-paid-leave. Accessed August 12, 2020.

2. University of Wisconsin Population Health Institute. Healthy workers, thriving Wisconsin: solutions addressing lack of income as a barrier to COVID-19 isolation and quarantine. 2021. Available at: https://uwphi.pophealth.wisc.edu/wp-content/uploads/sites/316/2021/01/HealthyWorkersThrivingWisconsin_FullReport.pdf. Accessed April 22, 2021.

3. Human Impact Partners and San Francisco Department of Public Health. A health impact assessment of the California Healthy Families, Healthy Workplaces Act of 2008: a case study. 2008. Available at: https://humanimpact.org/wp-content/uploads/2017/09/Healthy-Workplaces-Act-Case-Study-2008.pdf. Accessed August 12, 2020.

4. DeRigne LA, Stoddard-Dare P, Quinn L. Workers without paid sick leave less likely to take time off for illness or injury compared to those with paid sick leave. *Health Affairs*. 2016;35(3):520–27.

5. Kumar S, Quinn SC, Kim KH, et al. The impact of workplace policies and other social factors on self-reported influenza-like illness incidence during the 2009 H1N1 pandemic. *Am J Pub Health*. 2002;102(1):134–40.

6. Human Impact Partners. The health impacts of guaranteed paid sick days: a case story. December 2012. Available at: https://humanimpact.org/hipprojects/paid-sick-days-hias-case-story/?strategy=research. Accessed August 12, 2020.

7. Board of Governors of the Federal Reserve System. Report on the economic well-being of US households in 2018 – May 2019. 2019. Available at: https://www.federalreserve.gov/publications/2019-economic-well-being-of-us-households-in-2018-dealing-with-unexpected-expenses.htm. Accessed August 12, 2020

23

Environmental Health: Critical Issues for Our Children

Nsedu Witherspoon, MPH

Despite the many successes and advancements in the field of children's environmental health over the past few decades, today's children face an epidemic of illnesses and chronic diseases linked to environmental exposures and our changing climate. There is an urgent need to put children and their families at the forefront of our nation's actions related to public health and environmental health. A paradigm shift in the field of children's environmental health is required so that all levels of society work proactively to consider children and our future generations. A primary factor in making this shift is the need for effective state and national child protective policies.

Every day, we are exposed to dozens, perhaps hundreds, of chemicals. Toxic chemicals are found in the environment (air, water, and soil) and in food and consumer products. Since World War II, thousands of new, primarily synthetic, chemicals have been discovered and introduced into commerce and our environment. Chemicals are ubiquitous; traces of synthetic compounds are found in all humans and animals around the world.[1] Both synthetic and natural chemicals such as lead, once released into the environment, can harm the health of humans and wildlife. The diverse and growing range of chemicals to which we are exposed means that today's children live in an environment vastly different from previous generations. Currently more than 84,000 industrial chemicals and over 17,000 pesticide products are on the market in the United States. For the majority of these chemicals, little is known about their health effects on children.[2]

Exposures to toxic chemicals have been associated with harmful effects such as premature births, birth defects, developmental and learning disabilities, behavioral problems, obesity, asthma, digestive system diseases, and cancer.[3,4] As new chemicals are produced and dispersed into the environment, used in food production, or added to consumer products, the risk of toxic chemical exposure increases due to the prevalence and unknown safety of these chemicals. In addition, research on the effects of multiple exposures and cumulative risk is lacking.

CHILDREN ARE ESPECIALLY VULNERABLE

Children are especially vulnerable to the harmful health impacts of chemicals due to their developing physiology, unique behavioral characteristics, and special interactions with their environment. From the fetal stage through adolescence, children are in a dynamic state of growth as their immature nervous, respiratory, reproductive, and immune systems develop. Because of these developing systems, growing organisms can be more vulnerable to permanent and irreversible damage from toxicants than mature organisms. When growth and development are hampered, the chances of a healthy adulthood are dramatically decreased, as it is often impossible to repair damages that occur in childhood. The degree, route, and timing of exposure affects the response.

CHILDREN EXPERIENCE THE WORLD DIFFERENTLY

An infant more than doubles its weight in the first four months of life. Young children breathe more rapidly and take in more air, have higher metabolic rates, and have higher proportionate food and liquid intakes than do adults. Because children eat more fruits and vegetables and drink more liquids, potential exposure to toxins such as lead, pesticides, and nitrates is greater. Children exhibit hand-to-mouth behavior and are close to the ground where there may be more exposure to toxins in dust, soil, and carpets as well as to low-lying vapors such as radon or pesticides. Thus, in identifying how children may be exposed to a chemical and the level of exposure, it is inadequate to simply extrapolate from adult exposure.

There are existing disparities in children's health that are a direct product of poverty and structural racism. Children from low-income communities and communities of color often have greater risk of exposures to pollution, higher levels of contaminants in their bodies, and more illness or disability such as asthma and learning disabilities.

Higher body burdens of toxins increase the risk of developing certain diseases or disabilities, and children of color and from low-income families experience disproportionate adverse health outcomes. For example, the burdens of asthma fall more heavily on Black and Hispanic children. As of 2015, Black children (regardless of family income) reported higher rates of asthma than White children, according to the federal Office of Minority Health. Black children are reportedly four times more likely to be hospitalized for asthma and 10 times more likely to die of asthma than White children.[5] Learning disabilities such as dyslexia or impaired social skills are also more common among children from families with lower incomes. Child Trends researchers reported in 2013 that 16% of children living in families below the poverty line were identified as having a learning disability, compared with 6% of other children.[6]

Furthermore, children from underserved communities and communities of color are more susceptible to the adverse effects of climate change. This is due to inadequate investments in their neighborhoods, poor infrastructure, and residential segregation. Many are forced to live near hazardous waste sites, coal-fired power plants, or polluting industries, which can present significant exposure crises during natural disasters. Many in these communities lack the social and economic resources necessary to either relocate or to purchase the necessary materials or services to adapt to climate change where they are. As a result, children of color and from low-income families are at higher risk of suffering during extreme weather events, either due to direct harm from natural disasters or through potential increased air or drinking water pollution, food contamination, or from displacement, among other effects.[7]

CHALLENGES

A Blueprint for Protecting Children's Environmental Health: An Urgent Call for Action[8] is the Children's Environmental Health Network's (CEHN) framework that identifies and prioritizes the following recommendations.

Recommendation 1: Mobilize society to take action on children's environmental health; place a strong priority on children and families. There is an urgent need to transform society's understanding of children's environmental health and to put children and families at the forefront of society's conscience and thinking. The challenges include: (1) mobilizing society requires significant and long-term organizing; (2) scientific knowledge is not always translated in a way that is understood and accessible to the general public; and (3) families face multiple challenges yet public resources are scarce and policy attention is limited. The Children's Environmental Health Movement was launched by CEHN to address these recommendations.

Recommendation 2: Create knowledge essential for effective action and make use of the knowledge we have. Knowledge is critical for transformative change in children's environmental health. The challenges include: (1) credible and accessible information about children's environmental health is not collected in one place that is easily accessed by the public; (2) research on children's environmental health—including pediatric research and prevention—is often underfunded or is in some cases not funded at all. Applied research that would help develop effective public policy often falls outside of existing funding programs.

Recommendation 3: Marshal the engine of the economy to achieve environments in which children can thrive and enjoy abundant opportunity for building a sustainable, economically secure future. The challenges include: (1) manufacturing and production processes do not support the use of safer chemicals, and there is limited market demand for safer products; and (2) many businesses and trade associations deploy substantial resources to challenge protective policy efforts and undermine credible science. All of these realities must be addressed.

Recommendation 4: Build the political will in our institutions of government for child-centered policies. The primary challenge is that changing political will to embrace a societal issue—such as children's environmental health—requires a ground-swell of activity and support, as well as elevation of the value of children's environmental health among decision-makers.

EXAMPLE OF SUCCESS

Increasing amounts of research show that children are more heavily exposed than adults to toxicants such as pesticides. For example, studies that looked at biomarker levels for a commonly used organophosphate pesticide, chlorpyrifos, in children and adults found that the levels of the pesticide in children were substantially higher than in the adult population. Chlorpyrifos is a toxic, nerve-agent pesticide found to damage children's brain development, contaminate waterways, and injure wildlife—yet it is widely applied in the production of fruits, vegetables, nuts, and other conventionally grown crops, including child favorites like apples, peaches, grapes, and strawberries, as well as many vegetables.

Overwhelming scientific evidence demonstrates the detrimental effects of chlorpyrifos exposure to developing fetuses, infants, children, and pregnant women, including preterm birth, low birth weight, congenital abnormalities, pediatric cancers, asthma, and neurobehavioral and cognitive deficits such as lowered IQs, attention deficit/hyperactivity disorder (ADHD), and autistic disorders. If you are asking, "How is this pesticide not already banned?" you are not alone.

After years of study, the US Environmental Protection Agency (EPA) concluded that chlorpyrifos was unsafe at any level of exposure and proposed a rule to ban it.[9] The Trump administration overturned the recommendations of EPA's own scientists to ban its use—just weeks after taking office. In the face of federal inaction, several states have taken steps to ban chlorpyrifos. Hawaii was the first state to ban the pesticide, effective 2022. California banned use beginning January 31, 2020. Advocates in New York, Maryland, New Jersey, Vermont, Washington, and Oregon have also introduced bills to ban the use of chlorpyrifos. Globally, the European Union banned the sale and use of chlorpyrifos beginning January 31, 2020. These efforts continue to provide leadership in public health protections that will have positive implications for generations to come. CEHN has resources to assist with development of child protective policies available at www.cehn.org. Such policy actions are critical to safeguarding the health, safety, and wellness of current and future generations.

REFERENCES

1. Colborn T, Dumanoski D, Myers JP. *Our Stolen Future*. New York: Dutton; 1996.

2. US Environmental Protection Agency. About the TSCA chemical substance inventory. Available at: https://www.epa.gov/tsca-inventory/about-tsca-chemical-substance-inventory. Accessed September 21, 2020.

3. Renzo GCD, Conry JA, Blake J, et al. International Federation of Gynecology and Obstetrics opinion on reproductive health impacts of exposure to toxic environmental chemicals. *Int J Gynecol Obstet*. 2015;131(3):219–25.

4. DellaValle C. The pollution in people: cancer-causing chemicals in Americans' bodies. June 14, 2016. Available at: https://www.ewg.org/research/pollution-people. Accessed September 21, 2020.

5. US Department of Health and Human Services Office of Minority Health. Asthma and African Americans. Available at: https://minorityhealth.hhs.gov/omh/browse.aspx?lvl=4& lvlid=15#:~:text=In%202015%2C%20African%20American%20children,to%20non%2D Hispanic%20white%20children. Accessed June 6, 2020.

6. Child Trends Databank. Learning disabilities. 2014. Available at: https://www.childtrends .org/wp-content/uploads/2015/06/indicator_1435075028.197.pdf. Accessed September 21, 2020.

7. Morello-Frosch R, Pastor M, Sadd J, Shonkoff SB. The climate gap: inequalities in how climate change hurts Americans & how to close the gap. May 2009. Available at: https:// dornsife.usc.edu/assets/sites/242/docs/The_Climate_Gap_Full_Report_FINAL.pdf. Accessed December 12, 2017.

8. Children's Environmental Health Network. A blueprint for protecting children's environmental health: an urgent call for action. October 2015. Available at: https://cehn.org/wp-content/ uploads/2015/11/BluePrint_Final1.pdf. Accessed June 6, 2020.

9. Britton W, Drew D, Holman E, et al. Chlorpyrifos: revised human health risk assessment for registration review. November 17, 2016. Available at: https://www.regulations.gov/ document?D=EPA-HQ-OPP-2015-0653-0454. Accessed September 21, 2020.

24

Moving Elimination of Racism From the Margins to the Center of Health Policy

Gail C. Christopher, DN

Over the last four decades, I have worked, along with countless others, to help eliminate racial and ethnic health disparities and inequities. These efforts have encompassed issues that span the life course, from infant and maternal mortality to chronic disease burdens and environmental, food, and criminal justice; to education and public sector reform, voter suppression, immigration policy, affordable housing, and access to quality health care. Through health advocacy focused on health equity, disparity reduction, and social determinants, we have courageously identified and sought to alleviate the myriad consequences of racism.

As America seeks to bring equity to communities and advance social justice, it is vital that public health policy, advocacy, and budgeting decisions focus on racial equity and healing. With families and communities of color grieving the loss of loved ones from COVID-19 in astoundingly disproportionate percentages, a chorus of diverse voices are demanding that the nation take more direct action.

For too long, racism has been the root cause of health disparities and inequities that have ravaged populations of color. As recently as 1965, Black patients in some states could only receive care in separate and poorly funded medical facilities, where Black physicians were relegated to practice. When President Lyndon B. Johnson signed Medicare into law, more than 7,000 US hospitals instantly became subject to the civil rights regulations set in Title VI. These hospitals could no longer discriminate and receive federal payments for medical services. But the decades prior to that were periods of protracted defiance and resistance to integration.[1]

Systemic racism and unconscious bias continue to contribute to poor health outcomes for populations of color, with far too much suffering by individuals and their families, as infants die prematurely, chronic diseases ravage communities, and many lack health insurance. For example, Black people have higher mortality rates than any other racial or ethnic group for eight of the 10 leading causes of death.[2] We must jettison racism from our society and end its deleterious consequences and costs. Primary public health prevention of severe illness, disability, and death from COVID-19 requires minimizing exposure to the virus and optimizing protection to limit the potential for harm in environments of risk. In this regard, COVID-19 might be viewed as a metaphor for racism as a public health challenge. Primary prevention is also our domain for action. Public health workers must mobilize to curtail population exposure to cultural and systemic racism, while optimizing protective measures to limit and mitigate existing harms, thereby helping to prevent needless illness, disability, and excess deaths.

Clearly, the 21st century demands that we move beyond merely addressing the consequences of racism. It is time for the elimination of the false belief of racism; the cognitive, emotional, and embedded permission to minimize inherent value and humanity of groups of people within the human family. We must create a new model of relatedness that renders the antiquated notion of a hierarchy of human value obsolete, making racism and its attendant "isms"—xenophobia, sexism, religious bigotry, and anti-LGBTQisms—relics of the past. Our new model of relatedness requires work, skill, and capacity development within the public health profession, as well as within communities and jurisdictions across America. The Rx Racial Healing movement aims to generate a critical mass of people committed to working together and healing the wounds of the past as we seek to end racism and the inequities it has created.[3] Architect and systems thinker Buckminster Fuller once said: "You never change things by fighting the existing model. You must create a new model that makes the existing model obsolete."[4] By redefining racism as the embedded and entrenched belief system it is, Rx Racial Healing provides a needed on-ramp for launching the new model of relatedness that is grounded in the knowledge of our interconnected and equal worth as human beings. With this foundational idea in place, we can create new ways of living, policing, and governing, as well as ways of distributing resources more equitably because we recognize and value our collective common interests.

This is not a completely new type of work for public health as a field. We have been in the business of ethos, environment, and mass behavioral and culture change since our inception. The fact that life expectancy of Americans increased from 47 to 77 years over the course of the 20th century is primarily attributed to public health improvements such as better housing, sanitation systems, nutrition, and occupational safety.[5] The remaining gaps in health outcomes and life expectancy between racial and ethnic populations can also be largely attributed to a failure to make the elimination of racism and its systemic manifestations a public health priority.

JURISDICTIONS DECLARE RACISM A PUBLIC HEALTH CRISIS IN 2020

With the health disparities fueled by COVID-19 and the outrage caused by the death of George Floyd and others by police, the public health landscape is quickly changing. As of June 2020, counties and cities in at least 18 states in America had declared racism a public health crisis. In California, alone, 14 jurisdictions made this declaration.[6] This breakthrough can be attributed to the bold leadership by a diverse coalition of leaders in public health. All of our work to advance racial justice and the future viability of this experiment in democracy requires that we do it now and that we do it well.

Beyond declarations, cities are taking action to advance racial equity in communities. In Cleveland, Councilman Basheer Jones, one of the primary sponsors of the resolution, warned, "We better make sure this is not just a document, a piece of paper." In addition to declaring racism a public health crisis, the resolution establishes a group that is required to develop policy to address systemic racism that will lead to better health among Black communities.[7] In Somerville, Massachusetts, Mayor Joe Curtatone outlined several steps centered on reform at the police department, such as establishing a Civilian Oversight Committee to review use of force.[8] In Ypsilanti, Michigan, the city council declared,

> Racism unfairly disadvantages specific individuals and communities, while unfairly giving advantages to other individuals and communities, and saps the strength of the whole society through the waste of human resources, and the City of Ypsilanti's collective prosperity depends upon the equitable access to opportunity for every resident regardless of the color of their skin.[9]

The resolution calls for racial equity training for all City staff. It is evident there is renewed attention and commitment across communities to begin to dismantle the stronghold of systemic racism.

TRUTH, RACIAL HEALING & TRANSFORMATION

Our work with Truth, Racial Healing & Transformation (TRHT) provides a blueprint for actions by governments, businesses, and organizations that want to jettison racism and promote community and health equity. In 2017, TRHT was launched by the W.K. Kellogg Foundation with several local philanthropies. Leaders representing more than 150 organizations (including the American Public Health Association and the National Collaborative for Health Equity) worked together for seven months to create shared visions and a strategic guide for implementing TRHT that can be adapted by local jurisdictions.[10] As of 2020, 14 local jurisdictions, more than 40 college campuses, and more than 119 public libraries have engaged with or implemented TRHT-related efforts.[11]

TRHT Campus Centers are preparing the next generation of strategic leaders and thinkers to break down racial hierarchies and dismantle the belief in the hierarchy of human value. The American Society of Human Genetics issued a statement in 2018 declaring that the concept of "racial purity" or the belief in a hierarchy of human value is completely meaningless from a scientific standpoint.[12] The American Library Association

included a series on TRHT in their Great Stories Club, where libraries, community partners, and underserved teen audiences engage in reading and discussing theme-
related books and participating in programs led by a racial healing practitioner.[13] The
American Academy of Pediatrics filled in the huge gap when the CDC acknowledged
the social determinants of health impacting the quality of life for Americans, but omitted
the mental and physical harm from exposure to racism. The organization of 67,000 pedi-
atricians issued a policy statement declaring that "racism is a social determinant of
health" with a profound impact on the health status of children, adolescents, emerging
adults, and their families.[14]

In Congress, a House Resolution by Rep. Barbara Lee calls for creating a US
Commission on Truth, Racial Healing, and Transformation, which will examine the
effects of slavery, institutional racism, and discrimination against people of color, as well
as how our history impacts laws and policies today.[15]

HOW DOES PUBLIC HEALTH LEAD OUR NATION INTO THE NEEDED TRANSFORMATION?

Unlike in medical care, where the individual is the focus, the community— indeed, the
country—is the "patient" in public health strategies. As a result, work in the following
areas is needed to build the public will for sustaining efforts to ultimately eliminate racism and its consequences.

Narrative Change: The truth of the cause or source of the problem must be clearly identified and articulated. This part of the work has, to a large measure, begun thanks to the
courageous efforts of leaders of color in the health field. Activities date back to the
Reconstruction era.[16] Public health as a field knows that racism is the pathogenic virus.
This knowledge must now be shared more broadly and communicated to the general
public. Doing so requires creating a new narrative about health and a healthy society. We
must articulate and archive not only the horrific harms caused by racism, both historic
and contemporary; we must also clearly depict the unfair accumulation of benefits that
have accrued for dominant groups at the expense of the very lives of those suppressed
and killed, as well as their descendants. Equally important is a well-researched and articulated narrative of the collective benefits that all of America will accrue when racism and
fear no longer define our ethos.

Racial Healing: The level of societal eclipse that is needed requires exponential expansion of the circles of heartfelt engagement in this nation-saving work. Racial healing
brings diverse people together to develop and hone skills and capacities for experiencing
our common humanity through empathy and compassion.[17] People must learn how to
"see ourselves in the face of the other." These efforts at scale will generate the critical mass

of momentum required for changing systems and structures that are the pillars of the culture built by racism, an edifice of White racial hierarchy that continues to make lives of color invisible and exploitable. These pillars are separation, law, and economy.

Separation: Addressing structured and systemic separation is a key pillar in overcoming racism and is central to the Rx Racial Healing and TRHT work because a key characteristic of racial prejudice is an explicit desire to maintain social distance from defined groups.[18] Ironically, COVID-19 is giving the overall population an immersive experience in the stress, discomfort, and unnatural dynamics of social distancing. Research on bias and prejudice reduction recommends human interaction with people from the "perceived" other group as an effective intervention.[19] Creating and sustaining opportunities for cross-group engagement and connection is a cornerstone of the work of redesigning a culture that no longer embodies racial hierarchy once diverse people are living and working together. When eliminating racism is a priority, regional planning, economic development, transportation, and affordable housing projects all have public health implications. It is also critically important to deconcentrate poverty. This work can be advanced by utilizing public health tools such as assessments, policy interventions, and monitoring.

Law: A system of subjugation and oppression can only be sustained for centuries when the laws and powers governing that system authorize its maintenance. Critical Race Theory (CRT) developed in the 1970s and 1980s in the legal academy provides a clear analysis of how racial hierarchy is embedded in the legal structure of the United States of America. There have been calls to apply CRT to the health field.[20] Doing so could help the field better understand how racism must be addressed through the core functions of public health: assessment, policy development, and assurance. Racial impact assessments, discrimination and bias indices, and data measures of inequitable resource distribution would become standard practice. Intentional policies to end segregation and its many forms in housing, transportation systems, and access to quality air, food, and nature settings, as well as access to preventive and primary health care, would become the norm. Accountability for assuring and monitoring improvements and equity would become required. Related tools and performance expectations would be incorporated into public health education, training, hiring, and career advancement pathways. Moving racial equity and healing from the margins to the center of public health requires translating theory into practices that are authorized by laws, administrative regulations, and policies.

Economy: The third pillar and area of focus is the economy. Stolen land and centuries of forced, uncompensated labor were the hidden engines of American wealth and capitalism. Generational poverty and vast income, as well as wealth and asset inequities for families of color, are the result. Public health intersects with this manifestation of systemic racism on a daily basis as workers cope with disinvestment and resource disparities that create increased health risks in all the social determinants of health and well-being. If the nation eliminated racial disparities in health, education, incarceration, employment, and other areas, the gross domestic product of the United States could increase by $8 trillion by 2050, according to "The Business Case for Racial Equity: A Strategy for Growth."[21] This study concludes that racism and discrimination needlessly squander billions of dollars each year. In fact, a tremendous boost in consumer spending would occur if racial bias were no longer a barrier for people of color. The study showed better jobs, health, and education would spark an additional $191 billion of food purchases each year, $500 billion in spending on housing, $259 billion in spending on transportation, $77 billion in spending on entertainment, and $52 billion in spending on clothes. Further, local jurisdictions across the country would also experience a significant economic boom and better health outcomes by eliminating racial inequities.

EXAMPLES OF POLICIES AND PRACTICES THAT ADVANCE RACIAL EQUITY AND HEALING

The policies and practices described here align with the five components of the TRHT framework.

Narrative Change: Declarations by jurisdictions stating that racism is a public health crisis help shift public narratives regarding health inequities and disparities toward a more truthful root cause analysis. Requirements for racial equity impact assessments or related ordinances can help increase accountability for meaningful change.

One example of narrative changes comes from King County in Washington State. In 2010–11, the Martin Luther King County PLACE MATTERS[22] team led an effort to encourage the King County Council to pass an Equity and Social Justice Ordinance, which would require the county to prioritize equity and social justice in all decision-making. The first of its kind in the country, the Equity and Social Justice Ordinance has already changed many policy decisions undertaken by the Council to prioritize the needs of low-income communities and communities of color in ways that improve health and life opportunities for these residents. In August 2012, the County released its first report on the Ordinance,[23] which highlighted data and statistics showing inequities across the County and some of the County's accomplishments to date.

Alameda County, California, offers another example of narrative change. Supported by the Alameda County Public Health Department, Alameda PLACE MATTERS, East Oakland Building Healthy Communities (EOBHC), and other partners, Oakland City Councilwoman Desley Brooks proposed a new city department in 2015 to address systemic racism within the city government and in the city.[24]

Racial Healing: The purpose of racial healing activities is to expand circles of human engagement to increase the public and political will needed to support racial equity policy changes. This type of work is relational and focused on changing hearts and minds about the primacy of human value hierarchy and systemic racism and biases as causes of persistent inequity.

For example, the city of Richmond, Virginia, the epicenter of the Civil War, has been on a racial healing journey for decades. A hallmark of progress was the establishment by the city of a Slave Trail Commission and the development of previously unrecognized sites for commemorative education and healing activities. A reconciliation statue linking Liverpool, UK (the primary port involved in the transatlantic slave trade), and the Republic of Benin, Africa, now stands at the end of the trail. The trail led to ongoing dialogues, learning curricula, and related training models that serve Richmond and many other cities.[25]

Salinas, California, presents a unique approach to racial healing. In 2014, an innovative partnership between government, nonprofit, and philanthropy began in the city of Salinas, California—Healing-Informed Governing for Racial Equity. By combining racial healing with structural equity, proponents are determined to unlearn the scripted positions of city versus community, of us versus them. It is a significant and risky undertaking with potential for high impact. Local leaders made this bold move toward racial justice in response to a series of racially inflaming events, most notably four police-involved shootings of Latino men within a span of six months. Recognizing that a partnership is a process and not a product, insights are still unfolding. Thus far, the work has lifted up four key lessons:

1. Support community organizing and collective healing.
2. Balance racial healing and systemic equity.
3. Engage government staff at every level.
4. Build the "we" with shared language and experience.[26]

Separation: Historic and present-day land use and development decisions often perpetuate racial inequities. Related policy wins can have lasting impact for advancing equity.

For example, by doing away with single-family zoning, the City Council of Minneapolis, Minnesota, confronted its history of housing segregation.[27] Single-family zoning supports high rent practices, long commutes for employment, and racism in real estate. The new zoning policy addresses all these barriers to equity in one fell swoop. Single-family zoning was devised in the mid-20th century as a policy strategy to keep Black people and other marginalized racial and ethnic groups from moving into residential neighborhoods, and it still functions today. Abolishing restrictive zoning codes is a major policy step on the journey of addressing related damage and promoting more equitable opportunity for healthy living.

With the help of a national advocacy group, collaborating organizations and activists in Oakland, California, succeeded in redirecting $70 million in American Recovery and Reinvestment Act dollars away from a public transportation project that would have isolated low-income communities in Oakland toward public transportation that more effectively created equal opportunities by connecting previously marginalized communities to employment and education resources.[28]

Law: Local racial justice advocates work to protect the human and civil rights of people of color.

For example, youth organizations in Chicago and in California won policy victories for fairer public school disciplinary practices to limit excess school suspensions and expulsions of students of color for minor infractions such as dress code violations. The new code of conduct eliminated mandatory two-week suspensions for minor offenses and reduced the risk of criminalization by contact with the legal system. In Herndon, Virginia, local groups overturned an ordinance that criminalized day workers; in New Orleans, advocates succeeded in protecting the right to housing for displaced public housing residents.[29]

In politically divisive contexts, policy wins for racial equity often involve preventing the enactment of newly proposed discriminatory laws or preventing the roll back of previously won victories, such as those in fair housing or against voter suppression.

Economy: States and localities collect roughly one-third of the nation's taxes, and they account for nearly half of all domestic public sector spending. They also provide more than 90% of K–12 school funding and nearly all public college and university funding. States and localities own more than 90% of the country's non-defense public infrastructure, roads, and other transit systems, water systems, and airports, and they incarcerate more than 90% of the nation's prisoners. Fiscal policy at state and local levels is, perhaps, the most fertile ground for advancing racial equity and healing. However, city- and county-level activists or coalitions have limited influence on such major revenue decisions. Some local coalitions have fought successfully for living wage ordinances and tax limitations for low-income families, and for protections or increases in state Earned Income Tax Credit (EITC) benefits.[30] Two other examples of economic policy for racial equity are described here.

The Cuyahoga County, Ohio, PLACE MATTERS team successfully integrated its racial equity framework into the county's 2015 Health Improvement Partnership–Cuyahoga (HIP-C) plan.[31] Grounded in equity principles and based on local data, with meaningful input from community residents, the community health improvement plan provides strategic direction, action plans, and measurable outcomes. The Cuyahoga County team was instrumental in naming "Eliminating Racism as a Social Determinant of Health" as one of the four key priorities. Economic opportunity as a key social determinant of health is a core part of the health improvement plan.[32]

In 1993, the Florida House Speaker authorized funding for a research study and report on the Rosewood Massacre, which occurred January 1, 1923, in Rosewood, a small town in central Florida with about 150 Black residents. The massacre perpetrated by White people included burning most of the town. Any surviving residents fled. The report issued in 1993 motivated the Florida legislature to enact and the governor to sign legislation aimed toward granting equity, justice, fairness, and healing to survivors of the massacre, and it provided $2.1 million in reparations to survivors.[33]

CONCLUSION

Decades of working on the issue of racism and its health consequences have taught me that successful approaches must include a comprehensive framework that balances inherent tensions. We must not allow false dichotomies to hijack or derail efforts. Potential distractions include the following questions: Do we do relational work or keep a systemic and structural focus? Which oppressed groups' needs deserve to be prioritized? Are the voices of grassroots activists the most important, or should nonprofit leaders, academics, or public sector and private sector representatives be heard? Wisdom dictates that our strategies must accommodate these tensions with respect and responsive direction. I have focused on eliminating the undergirding, yet false, belief in human value hierarchy that permits persistent racial injustice. I have applied a framework that supports policy and practice changes while expanding circles of human understanding and engagement. I have learned that real change is possible, and it is happening. The work must be brought to scale, and it must continue to be informed by the lived experiences of diverse communities who bear the disproportionate burden of this public health crisis. But I remain convinced that Dr. Martin Luther King's vision will be actualized within our lifetime.

REFERENCES

1. Largent E, Association of Schools and Programs of Public Health. Public health, racism and the lasting impact of hospital segregation. *Public Health Reports.* 2018;133(6):715–20.

2. US Department of Health and Human Services Office of Minority Health. Minority population profiles: Black/African Americans. Available at: https://www.minorityhealth.hhs.gov/omh/browse.aspx?lvl=3&lvlid=61. Accessed May 3, 2021.

3. Christopher G. Commission on security and cooperation in Europe (Helsinki Commission): briefing on truth, reconciliation and healing: toward a unified future. July 18, 2019. Available at: https://drgailcchristopher.com/Commission-on-security-and-cooperation-in-europe-Helsinki-Commission. Accessed October 26, 2020.

4. Sieden LS. *A Fuller View: Buckminster Fuller's vision of hope and abundance for all.* Studio City, CA: Divine Arts; 2012.

5. Centers for Disease Control and Prevention. Ten great public health achievements, 1900 to 1999. *MMWR.* 1999;48:241–43.

6. American Public Health Association. Declarations of racism as a public health issue. Available at: http://www.apha.org/topics-and-issues/Health Equity/racism and health/racism-declarations. Accessed October 26, 2020.

7. Higgs R. Declaring racism a health crisis in Cleveland labeled a start; the real work will be finding the solutions. June 5, 2020. Available at: https://www.cleveland.com/cityhall/2020/06/declaring-racism-a-health-crisis-in-cleveland-labeled-a-start-the-real-work-will-be-finding-the-solutions.html. Accessed October 26, 2020.

8. The Telegraph. Massachusetts town declares racism a public health emergency. June 4, 2020. Available at: https://www.thetelegraph.com/news/article/Massachusetts-town-declares-racism-a-public-15317549.php. Accessed November 1, 2020.

9. City of Ypsilanti. Minutes: Virtual Council Meeting. June 2, 2020. Available at: https://cityofypsilanti.com/AgendaCenter/ViewFile/Minutes/_06022020-1392. Accessed July 16, 2021.

10. W.K. Kellogg Foundation. Restoring to wholeness: racial healing for ourselves, our relationships, and our communities. 2018. Available at: https://www.wkkf.org/resource-directory/resources/2018/02/restoring-to-wholeness--racial-healing-for-ourselves--our-relationships-and-our-communities--trht. Accessed October 26, 2020.

11. Christopher G. Believing and creating the "we" in we hold these truths: dismantling racial hierarchies, building equitable communities. McNair T, ed. 2020. Available at: https://www.tfah.org/wp-content/uploads/2020/07/WeHoldTheseTruths_AACU.pdf. Accessed October 26, 2020.

12. American Society of Human Genetics. ASHG denounces attempts to link genetics and racial supremacy. *Am J Hum Genet.* 2018;103(5):636.

13. Cecire M, Ashihei W, Campbell E, Centeno V. Deeper than our skins: the present is a conversation with the past. American Library Association, Great Stories Club. 2019. Available at: http://www.ala.org/tools/programming/greatstories/resources/skins. Accessed October 26, 2020.

14. Trent M, Dooley DG, Douge J. The impact of racism on child and adolescent health. *Pediatrics.* 2019;144(2):e20191765.

15. 116th Congress 2d Session H. CON.RES. Urging the establishment of a United States Commission on truth, racial healing, and transformation concurrent resolution. Available at: https://Lee.house.gov/. Accessed October 26, 2020.

16. Ford CL, Griffith DM, Bruce MA, Gilbert KL. *Racism: science & tools for the public health professional.* Washington, DC: APHA Press; 2019.

17. Christopher G. Racial healing circles: empathy and liberal education. *Diversity Democracy.* 2018;21(3):10–13.

18. Pettigrew TL, Meettens R. Subtle and blatant prejudice in Western Europe. *Eur J Soc Psychol.* 1995;25(1):57–75.

19. Marcelin JR, Siraj DS, Victor R, Kotadia S, Maldonado YA. The impact of unconscious bias in healthcare: how to recognize and mitigate it. *J Infect Dis.* 2019;220(Suppl 2):S62–S73.

20. Obasogie O, Heaven I, Mujahid M. Race, law and health disparities: toward a critical race intervention. *Ann Rev Law Soc Sci.* 2017;13:313–29.

21. Turner A. The business case for racial equity: a strategy for growth. Battle Creek, MI: W.K. Kellogg Foundation and Altarum; 2018. Available at: https://www.wkkf.org/resource-directory/resource/2018/07/business-case-for-racial-Equity. Accessed October 26, 2020.

22. National Collaborative for Health Equity. Community strategies to end racism and support racial healing: the place matters approach to promoting racial equity. Available at: https://www.nationalcollaborative.org/wp-content/uploads/2016/02/Community-Strategies-to-End-Racism-and-Support-Racial-Healing-The-Place-Matters-Approach-to-Promoting-Racial-Equity-.pdf. Accessed October 26, 2020.

23. King County Executive Office. *Equity and Social Justice Annual Report.* August 2012. https://www.racialequitytools.org/resourcefiles/EquityReport2012_(2).pdf. Accessed October 26, 2020.

24. Epstein K. Victory for Oakland's new department of race and equity. June 28, 2015. Available at: https://blog.oaklandxings.com/2015/06/victory-for-oaklands-new-department-of-race-and-equity/. Access date needed.

25. Corcoran R. *Trust building: an honest conversation on race, reconciliation and responsibility* Richmond: University of Virginia Press; 2010.

26. Dieng JB, Valenzuela J, Ortiz T. Building the we: healing informed government for racial equity in Salinas. Race Forward: The Center for Racial Justice Innovation. Available at: https://www.raceforward.org/system/files/pdf/reports/BuildingTheWe.pdf. Accessed October 26, 2020.

27. Grabar H. Minneapolis confronts its history of housing segregation. December 7, 2018. Available at: https://slate.com/business/2018/12/minneapolis-single-family-zoning-housing-racism.html. Accessed October 26, 2020.

28. McDowell C, et al. Advancing the work: America healing: WKKF's investments in racial equity and racial healing 2009-2014. Boston: Interaction Institute for Social Change. 2014: 19–20.

29. Inouye TE, et al. Five-year retrospective grant analysis of the W.K. Kellogg Foundation's racial equity grant-making. Oakland, CA: Social Policy Research Associates; 2014:46–47.

30. Leachman M, Mitchell M, Johnson N, Williams E. Advancing racial equity with state tax policy. Center on Budget and Policy Priorities. November 15, 2018. Available at: https://www.cbpp.org/research/state-budget-and-tax/advancing-racial-equity-with-state-tax-policy. Accessed September 28, 2020.

31. HIP Cuyahoga. Available at: http://www.hipcuyahoga.org. Accessed September 28, 2020.

32. HealthEquityGuide.org. Cuyahoga County uses health improvement process to lift up equity and racial inclusion. Available at: https://healthequityguide.org/case-studies/cuyahoga-county-uses-health-improvement-process-to-lift-up-equity-and-racial-inclusion/. Accessed September 28, 2020.

33. Rosewood Massacre, a harrowing tale of racism and the road toward reparations. *Guardian*. January 2, 2016. Available at: https://www.theguardian.com/us-news/2016/jan/03/rosewood-florida-massacre-racial-violence-reparations. Accessed October 26, 2020.

25

Conclusion: Framing the Future of Public Health Policy

Grace Guerrero Ramirez, MSPH and Grace Castillo, MPH

The COVID-19 crisis has disrupted and damaged the United States in ways that would have seemed implausible in January 2020. Our inability to curtail COVID-19's impact stems from an abysmal partisan response and decades of harmful policies and unaddressed health inequities. These inequities have been created and exacerbated by racist and oppressive policies sponsored by governments and corporate interests—these policies are working exactly as they were designed. Equally responsible for COVID-19's devastation in the United States is the divestment in our nation's public health infrastructure, depleting us of necessary resources and limiting our state and local governmental public health agencies' capacity to mitigate and respond to intersecting crises. The American death toll—over 560,000 as of this writing—wasn't inevitable, but our policies certainly made this tragedy far more likely. Leadership across the political and public health spectrum must remain focused on the policy changes needed to ensure the nation is better prepared for the next natural or human-made disaster.

As COVID-19 and many other crises have made undeniably clear, we must recognize that public health is political. This understanding will better equip our field to explore bold pathways for change. The contributing authors in this book have reflected on the skills, knowledge, and perspectives needed as we begin the process to review and propose the policies that are conducive to a healthier nation.

In this book, the authors have explored distinct powers and constraints of federal, state, and local governments. At the federal level, advocates may focus their efforts on ensuring the effective and equitable use of federal powers to embed health and equity across governmental sectors and provide fair public health and health care funding. At the state level, health departments are uniquely positioned to develop, implement, and evaluate innovative policies, leverage data, and deploy resources across systems—all in spite of budget cuts and dwindling resources. While federal and state policy wins are crucial to sustainable change, the experiences described in San Antonio demonstrate that we should not underestimate the power of action at the local level, which often serves as a precursor to state and federal policy gains. CityHealth, the Centers for Disease Control and Prevention's Health Impact in 5 Years initiative (HI-5), and the Promoting Health and Cost Control in States (PHACCS) project offer road maps for equitable and evidence-based health policy approaches that public health champions and policymakers can model in their jurisdictions.

The authors have highlighted the importance of political engagement, regulatory action, and litigation, which can also be mutually reinforcing mechanisms, to advance health policy. Public health's role in legislative and political actions, including campaigns and electoral politics, cannot be overstated. Indeed, there is a call for more public health professionals to run for office and ensure the prioritization of public health in all policies. Meanwhile, regulatory policy has proven to be a powerful approach to hold industries accountable to the public, although it often has been used in the service of political rather than public health interests. Used appropriately, litigation is another important tool to ensure industry and governmental transparency, generate revenue to fund public health programs and services, and fight harmful governmental policies.

This book features voices from the public health and advocacy fields as they effectively communicated urgency, partnered with community and political stakeholders, launched advocacy campaigns, and built coalitions to address upstream challenges. Policy wins included securing funding for improved data infrastructure, passing sound gun safety legislation, and advancing policies for racial justice. A consistent theme across chapters is the importance of science and evidence—and defending it vehemently when attacked—to support policies intended to create healthier communities. However, data and numbers alone rarely change hearts and minds. The case studies and stories portrayed in this book stress the importance of persistence, shifting power to communities, building cross-sector partnerships, and sharing stories that resonate with the people that we need on public health's side.

The newly revised 10 Essential Public Health Services explicitly positions equity at the center of all public health tasks and approaches.[1] This recent change highlights the need to normalize and institutionalize work toward achieving equity as explicitly the work, and domain, of public health. Prioritizing equity when developing policy cannot be an afterthought. Several authors have discussed the need to ensure that health and racial equity are explicitly embedded and impacted communities are engaged throughout the policy lifecycle of creation, implementation, and evaluation. Centering health equity also requires public health practitioners to understand when to step up and when to step aside in support of community members who have to bear the brunt of racist and inequitable systems and who are leading the work of racial and social justice. We must prioritize community leadership and ownership every step of the way. Importantly, building health and racial equity as a process requires robust mechanisms to ensure accountability throughout the policy development process, including implementation.

Many local governments, corporations, and public health entities have declared racism a public health crisis, but those declarations must be followed by action leading to structural change. It's imperative to use our public health expertise, platforms, and advocacy at the service of racial justice, and to act with courage, humility, and strong resolve to build anti-oppressive health, education, economic, and legal systems. With the inauguration of the nation's 46th president, we are gripped by uncertainty, mass unrest, and systemic violence. This time urges public health practitioners to be bold, loud, and creative to elevate and sustain a unified movement for health equity, and to co-construct new structures and policies that pursue justice.

Policy may appear to be an elusive and even intimidating point of action. But, when used effectively, policy can accelerate our progress to a more just, equitable, and healthier society. Our hope is that this book prompts you to reflect on our individual and collective capacity to effect transformative change, and that it provides practical access to a variety of levers at our disposal to not just improve the world we have but to build the world we want. Remember, programs and interventions cannot fix what decades, if not centuries, of policy has broken. Only policy can fix what policy has broken.

REFERENCES

1. 10 Essential Public Health Services Future Initiative Task Force. The 10 essential public health services. September 2020. Available at: https://phnci.org/uploads/resource-files/EPHS-English.pdf. Accessed September 30, 2020.

Contributors

Rex Archer, MD, MPH
Director of Health, Kansas City Health Department

Marice Ashe, JD, MPH
Public health law consultant; Founder, ChangeLab Solutions (retired)

John Auerbach, MBA
President and CEO, Trust for America's Health

W. Steven Barnett, PhD
Senior Co-Director and Founder, National Institute for Early Education Research;
Board of Governors Professor, Graduate School of Education, Rutgers University

Georges Benjamin, MD
Executive Director, American Public Health Association

Colleen Bridger, MPH, PhD
Assistant City Manager, City of San Antonio

Derek Carr, JD
Senior Attorney, ChangeLab Solutions

Grace Castillo, MPH
Program Associate, de Beaumont Foundation

Brian C. Castrucci, DrPH
President and CEO, de Beaumont Foundation

Gail C. Christopher, DN
Executive Director, National Collaborative for Health Equity

Stacie Duitsman, MPH
Kansas City Health Department

Abdul El-Sayed, MD, DPhil
Former Health Director, City of Detroit

Lili Farhang, MPH
Co-Director, Human Impact Partners

Todd Fraley, JD
Senior Policy Analyst, Chicago Department of Public Health

Ellen Frede, PhD
Senior Co-Director, National Institute for Early Education Research; Research Professor, Graduate School of Education, Rutgers University

Grace Guerrero Ramirez, MSPH
Former Fellow, Association of Schools and Programs of Public Health, de Beaumont Foundation

Patrick Guerriero
Founding Partner, Civitas

Shelley Hearne, DrPH
Deans Sommer and Klag Professor of the Practice for Public Health Advocacy; Director, Center for Public Health Advocacy, Johns Hopkins Bloomberg School of Public Health

Jonathan Heller, PhD
Senior Health Equity Fellow, University of Wisconsin Population Health Institute; Co-Founder, Human Impact Partners

Emily J. Holubowich, MPP
Vice President, Federal Advocacy, American Heart Association; Founder and Former Director, Data: Elemental to Health Campaign

Edward L. Hunter, MA
Public health and health policy consultant

David H. Jernigan, PhD
Professor, Department of Health Law, Policy and Management, Boston University School of Public Health; Senior Policy Advisor, CityHealth

Maria Levis-Peralta, MPH, MPA, PCMH-CCE
Chief Executive Officer, Impactivo

Adam Lustig, MS
Manager, Promoting Health and Cost Control in States, Trust for America's Health

Dannel P. Malloy, JD
Former Governor of Connecticut

Christiana K. McFarland, PhD
Research Director, Center for City Solutions, National League of Cities

Ron Nirenberg, MA
Mayor of San Antonio

Catherine Patterson, MPP
Co-Executive Director, CityHealth

Susan L. Polan, PhD
Associate Executive Director, Public Affairs and Advocacy, American Public Health Association

Karen Remley, MD, MBA, MPH
Professor of Pediatrics, Eastern Virginia Medical School; Former Virginia Commissioner of Health

Meghan Roney, MPH
Program Services Manager, Non-Infectious Disease Programs, CDC Foundation

Joshua M. Sharfstein, MD
Vice Dean for Public Health Practice and Community Engagement, Johns Hopkins Bloomberg School of Public Health

Elizabeth L. Skillen, PhD, MS
Senior Policy Advisor, Office of the Associate Director for Policy and Strategy, Centers for Disease Control and Prevention

Kendall Stagg, JD
Director of Community Health, Kaiser Permanente

Monica Valdes Lupi, JD, MPH
Managing Director, Kresge Foundation's Health Program

Jake Williams, MS
Executive Director, Healthier Colorado

Nsedu Witherspoon, MPH
Executive Director, Children's Environmental Health Network

Index

A

abortions, 72
absentee voting, 58
accountability
  of elected officials, 119
  government, 67, 116
  policy, 119
achievement gap, 135
An Act Concerning Gun Violence and Children's Safety, 126
addiction treatment, 51
administration, 43, 61, 70
  anti-science, 63, 110, 156
  vaccine, 20
Administrative Procedures Act, 11, 63
adverse childhood experiences (ACEs), 22, 40
advocacy
  in action, 99
    embracing incrementalism, 113–116
    #SpeakForHealth, 107–111
    policy impact through strong legal practice, 117–120
    public health funding coalitions, 101–105
  campaigns, 115, 117
  community-based, 4
  Data, 103–105
  groups, 43
  lobbying and, 110
  national, 113
  public health, 1, 7–11, 58, 62, 69, 92
affirmative action, 77
affirmative litigation, 68–70, 68f, 77–78
Affordable Care Act, 19, 75
Age-Friendly Public Health, 22

air
  clean, 36, 61
  pollution, 69
alcohol, 9, 119
  pricing strategies, 50f
  sales, 34, 84–86, 88
  tax, 52
All Hands on Deck, 109
American Academy of Pediatrics, 162
American Cancer Society, 26
American Heart Association, 26
American Israel Public Affairs Committee, 116
American Library Association, 161
American Public Health Association (APHA), 92, 107, 109, 161
American Recovery and Reinvestment Act of 2009, 101, 165
American Rescue Plan Act, 105
American Society of Human Genetics, 161
amicus curiae, 68
anchor institution, 9
Association of Public Health Laboratories (APHL), 103
Association of State and Territorial Health Officials (ASTHO), 43
asthma, 34, 41, 131, 133, 153–154
attention deficit hyperactivity disorder (ADHD), 156

B

background checks, 126, 128
de Beaumont Foundation, 34, 84, 102
behaviors, 39, 50f, 51–52, 135, 142, 153
benzodiazepines, 62
bias indices, 163
bipartisan support, 34, 114

birth, 153

Black Lives Matter, 94

Blueprint for Protecting Children's Environmental
   Health, 155

Buffer Zone ordinance, 74–75

BUILD Health Challenge, 117

Burke-Harris, Dr., 22

"The Business Case for Racial Equity," 164

C

California Healthy Families, Healthy Workplaces Act,
   148–149

California Work and Family Coalition, 148

Campaign for Tobacco-Free Kids, 26

cancer, 26, 83, 153

ceiling preemption, 83–84

censored terminology, 107

Center for Environmental Health, 69–70

Center for Medicare and Medicaid Services, 61

Center on Alcohol Marketing and Youth, 88

Centers for Disease Control and Prevention (CDC),
   15, 39, 42, 103, 171

   "CDC gets list of forbidden words" (Washington
      Post), 107

   Coalition, 107

   Foundation, 40, 43–45

   HI-5 and, 43

ChangeLab Solutions, 120

Chief Health Strategist (CHS), 19, 20, 22

child abuse, 135, 153

Childhood Lead Poisoning Prevention Program, 131

Children's Environmental Health Network (CEHN),
   155–156

chlorpyrifos, 156

cigarette, 69

   electronic, 63, 70, 87, 101, 104, 108

   menthol, 74–75

   policies, 34

CityHealth, 25–26, 85, 86, 171

   framework

      policy, 34–37, 36f

      progress of, 36

      social determinants and social needs in, 33–34

   initiative, 137

   preemption and, 84

   2021 policy package updates, 37

Civilian Oversight Committee, 161

civil rights, 166

civil unions, 115

climate

   change, 19, 109, 153

   mitigation, 67

community, 2, 4, 89, 109

   of color, 39

   engagement, 118

   health, 7, 117

   interventions, 41

   low-income, 154

Community Guide, 41

community-wide interventions (CWIs), 40, 42

commuting zones, 85

Congress, 11, 16

Constitution, 7, 8, 11

Consumer Product Safety Commission, 61–62

contraception, 63, 72

Coronavirus Aid, Relief, and Economic Security
      (CARES) Act, 16, 105

correctional facilities, 20

Cost of Preschool Program Quality Calculator, 139

Council of State and Territorial Health
         Epidemiologists (CSTE), 102–103

County Health Rankings and Roadmaps, 41

COVID-19 pandemic, 2–3, 3f, 10, 14, 71, 101, 150, 163

   CARES Act, 16, 105

   data modernization and, 105

   death toll, 171

   economic disruption from, 33

   grieving loss of loved ones from, 159

   health disparities fueled by, 160

   health opportunity gap during, 33

   impact of, 49, 171

   paid sick leave laws during, 35, 87, 147

   public health and, 67, 91, 96

   response, 16, 29

criminal justice reform, 128, 159

Critical Race Theory (CRT), 163

Curtatone, Joe, 161

D

data

   analysis, 43

   collection, 20

entry, 102
exchange, 101
infrastructure, 101
modernization, 103–105
sharing of, 9, 103
sources, 20
systems, 22
transparency, 120
Data: Elemental to Health advocacy campaign,
    103–105
decision-making, evidence-based, 107
defensive litigation, 68f, 70–72
Deferred Action for Childhood Arrivals (DACA)
    program, 75
de jure policy, 76
Department of Agriculture, 61
Department of Behavioral Health, 142
Department of Corrections, 142
Department of Health and Human Services (HHS), 39
Department of Housing and Urban Development
    (HUD), 15, 43, 86, 133
Department of Justice, 11
developmental delays, 136
developmental disabilities, 153
diabetes, 25
Dialogue4Health, 42
digestive system diseases, 153
disaster relief funding, 15–16
discrimination, 1, 162
disease, 35, 88
    blood-borne, 51
    chronic, 13, 159
    clusters, 2
    disproportionate burden of, 3
    surveillance, 20
    transmission, 148
    vaccine-preventable, 101, 108
domestic violence, 35, 127
"Driving Public Health in the Fast Lane," 102–103
Dual Eligible program, 14
due process, 11
dyslexia, 154

E

early childhood education (ECE)
    Head Start program, 136

NIEER, 137
    pre-Kindergarten programs, 50f, 51, 84,
        135–140, 138t
Earned Income Tax Credits (EITCs), 40, 50f, 53, 166
    Action Guide, 43
    eligible recipients, 44
    "Health Impact in Five Years (HI-5)," 43
    health impacts of, 44
    policy, 44
    Public Health Action Guide, 44
Ebola, 101
economic disparities, 1, 15, 39, 166–167
economic disruption, 33
economic instability, 1
economic prosperity, 37
economic security, 35–36, 43, 147–150
economic well-being, 50f, 51, 53
economy, 163–164
education, 2, 34–36, 128, 159
    access to, 39
    disparities, 1
    early, 4
    ECE pre-Kindergarten programs, 50f, 51, 84,
        135–140, 138t
    PHACCS Initiative and, 51
    for public health practitioners, 19, 78
    quality of, 39, 83
electronic health records, 101
"Eliminating Racism as a Social Determinant of
    Health," 166
emergency
    contraception, 63
    declarations, 20
    relief funding, 13, 15–16, 102
    response, 19
emigration, from Puerto Rico, 13
emissions, 57, 61, 63
employer health programs, 9
environment, 9, 51–52, 61
environmental exposures, 2, 153, 159
environmental health
    challenges, 155–156
    critical issues for children, 153–156
environmental inspections, 64
environmental justice, 67
Environmental Protection Agency (EPA), 61, 156

environmental regulations, 75
epidemic
opioid, 19–21
sequential, 2
epidemiology, 19
equality
under law, 94
marriage, 113, 115–116
Equitable Enforcement to Achieve Health
Equity, 120
Equity and Social Justice Ordinance, 164
eviction moratoriums, 71

F

Families First Coronavirus Response Act, 87, 147
family
leave, paid, 50f, 53
low-income, 40
federal funding caps, 16
federal government, 7, 11
emergency funds, 13, 15–16, 102
Federal Medical Assistance Percentage
(FMAP), 14
federal policies, 9, 11
adverse impact on health, migration,
and economy
case of Puerto Rico, 13–17
emergency and disaster relief funding,
15–16
federal poverty level, 14–15
federal responsibility, 10
federal spending, 10
Federal Transit Administration, 43
First Amendment to the US Constitution, 73, 77
Flint water crisis, 57
floor preemption, 83–84
Floyd, George, 160
food
access to, 34
insecurities, 3
safe and healthy, 34, 36, 40
supply, 61
Food and Drug Administration (FDA), 61, 63, 70
food vending, healthy, 34, 84–85
foreign policy, 10
Fuller, Buckminster, 160

G

gag order, 108, 110
generational poverty, 57, 163
"Generation Public Health," 108–109
glasses, free, 57
government, 19, 75–76
accountability, 67, 116
authority, 67
federal, 7, 11, 13, 15–16, 102
judiciary, 67
levels of, 8
powers of, 7, 67
Great Stories Club, 161
Griffith, Morgan, 142
gun reform, 93
background checks, 126, 128
laws, 125–126, 128
safety
An Act Concerning Gun Violence and Children's
Safety, 126
legislation, 172
mass shootings and, 125–128
violence, 125, 127
assault weapons, 126

H

H1N1 virus outbreak, 20, 149
Hamilton, Alexander, 7
harm reduction, 50f, 51–52
Harvard T.H. Chan School of Public Health, 96
#SpeakForHealth, 107–111
Head Start program, 136
Healing-Informed Governing for Racial Equity, 165
health
data, 101
determinants, 2
disparities, 34, 37, 44
equity, 9, 21–22, 40, 96, 117, 159, 172
hazards, 43
impact, 51
inequities, 1, 21, 49–53, 50f, 148
officials, 19–22
opportunity gap, 33
outcomes, 9, 39, 40, 43, 159
philanthropy, 94

policy, 1, 20
prevention, 11
strategists, 10, 19–22
health care
access to, 1–2, 40, 93, 115, 128, 135
universal, 57
barriers to, 49
community, 7
costs, 2, 25
equitable, 4
expenditures, 2
funding disparities, 15
improvement through policy change, 4, 37
learning and, 50f
promotion, 49
providers, 15, 92
system, 7
Healthcare Information and Management Systems
Society (HIMSS), 103
Health Enterprise/Equity Zone (HEZ), 22
Healthier Colorado, 91–98
Health Impact Assessment (HIA), 147–150
"Health Impact in Five Years (HI-5)," 43
Health Impact in Five Years (HI-5) Model, 39, 41f, 171
CWIs, 40, 42–44
development of, 41–42
essential skills for next-generation public health
practice, 44–45
multisector collaboration for, 42–44
Partner Consortium, 40, 43, 45
policy as essential public health function, 42
health information technology (HIT), 20, 103
Health Information Technology for Economic and
Clinical Health (HITECH) Act, 101
health insurance plans, 10, 159
Healthy Air and Water Colorado, 96
Healthy Homes Rental Inspection Program, 131–134
Healthy People 2030, 39, 44
hearing testing, 137
heart disease, 41
hepatitis B virus, 52
hepatitis C virus, 52
hexavalent chromium, 69
hiring protections, 50f
HIV prevention services, 21
Hockley, Nicole, 126

homelessness, 20
home mortgage lending, 117
housing, 70
affordable, 34–36, 51–53, 83–86
HUD, 15, 43, 86, 133
rehabilitation loan and grant programs, 50f, 53
rental inspection policy, 131, 134
healthy homes rental program, 132–133
safe, 39–40, 50f, 83
unstable, 39
Housing First, 53
Housing Rehabilitation Loan and Grant Programs,
50f, 53
human immunodeficiency virus, 52
Human Impact Partners (HIP), 147–148, 150
human rights, 166
human value hierarchy, 167

I

illness
chronic, 108
prevention, 2
immigration policy, 10, 67, 117
DACA program, 75
immunization. See vaccination
inclusionary zoning, 34, 83–86
incrementalism, 113–116
infant mortality, 159
infectious disease
through immigration, 10
outbreak, 35
reportable, 20
inter-governmental litigation, 75
Internal Revenue Service, 40
interpersonal violence, 150
interstate commerce, 10
interstate travel, restrictions on, 67
interventions, 41–42
CWIs, 40
evidence-based, 25
policy-level, 25
public health, 101

J

James, Sly, 132
Jefferson, Thomas, 8

Jim Crow segregation, 77
Johnson, Lyndon B., 159
Jones, Basheer, 161
judiciary government, 67
Juul e-cigarettes, 70

K

Kaine, Tim, 141–143
Kaiser Permanente, 34, 84
King, Martin Luther, 164, 167

L

labor standards, 67
land use planning, 117
laws
    criminal, 117
    enforcement of, 61, 118–120
    equality under, 94
    exclusionary, 4
    gun, 125–126, 128
    new, 61
    nondiscrimination, 113, 116
    paid sick leave, 35, 87, 147
    public health and, 67
    regulations for, 61, 63
    state, 83–89
    tobacco, 25, 71, 87–88
lead
    Childhood Lead Poisoning Prevention
        Program, 131
    in children's products, 69
    exposure, 153
    in instruments, 69
    mitigation, 57
    poisoning, 61, 69, 131
    sources of, 34
    testing in schools, 57
    in water, 70
learning disabilities, 153–154
Lee, Barbara, 162
legal advice, 64
legislation, 62
    gun safety, 125–126, 172
    regulatory action and, 64
    safe school, 116

lesbian, gay, bisexual, and transgender (LGBT)
        movement, 113–116
life expectancy, 1, 4, 85
litigation, 4, 11, 172
    power of, 67
        affirmative, 68–70, 68f, 77–78
        defensive, 68f, 70–72
        inter-governmental, 75–76
        opportunities and challenges in public health,
            76–77
        strategic hybrid: quasi-defensive, 68f,
            72–75, 73f
    public health, 68f
lobbyists, 27, 110
local action, in policy change, 25–29
local health policy, preemption and, 88–89
low-income subsidy, 14
lung cancer, 83

M

marriage equality, 113, 115–116
mask-wearing, in public spaces, 97
mass shooting, 125–128
Master Settlement Agreement, 69, 76
maternal mortality, 159
measles, 101
Medicaid, 11, 13–16
Medicare, 10, 16, 159
    Advantage, 11, 13
    underfunding implications for aging population,
        13–14
medication-assisted therapy, 51
menthol cigarettes, 74–75
migration, 13–14
minimum wage, 1, 76, 132, 150
multisector collaboration, 42–43

N

naloxone, 21, 51
narrative change, 162, 164
National Association for Public Health Statistics
        and Information Systems
        (NAPHSIS), 103
National Association of County and City Health
        Officials (NACCHO), 43

National Collaborative for Health Equity, 161
National Institute for Early Education Research
    (NIEER), 137, 138t, 139
National League of Cities, 132
National Network of Public Health Institutes
    (NNPHI), 43
National Prevention, Health Promotion, and Public
    Health Council, 10
National Public Health Week, 109
National Rifle Association (NRA), 116, 126–127
National Smoke-Free Day, 143
natural disasters, 101
neglect, 135
nondiscrimination laws, 113, 116
Northam, Ralph, 142–143
nutrition, 70, 135
    decisions, 34
    inadequate, 1
    school, 50f, 51
    SNAP, 9
Nutrition Labeling and Education Act, 74

O

Obama Administration, 61
obesity, 25, 108, 153
Office of Management and Budget, 11
Office of Minority Health, 154
opioid
    crisis, 51, 62, 104, 108
    epidemic, 19–20
    litigation, 69
    manufacturers, 69
    misuse, 101
    prescription, 69
organophosphate pesticide, 156
overdose, 51, 77
OxyContin, 69

P

partisan divide, 114–115, 171
patient outcomes, 33
personal liberty, 28
pesticides, 154, 156
pharmaceutical industry, 61, 77
philanthropic foundations, 92

physical environment, 39
PLACE MATERS, 164, 166
police reform policy, 93
policy
    action, 4, 8
    change, 2–3
    city-level, 34
    decisions, 3f
    development, 42
    evidence-based, 4, 39, 107
    exclusionary, 1, 4
    federal, 5–11, 13–17, 19–22, 25–29
    health-promoting, 83
    impact, 1, 34, 117–120
    legislative, 4
    lobbyists and, 27
    local, 5–11, 13–17, 19–22, 25–29
    people-centered, 114
    power of, 4
    public health and, 4, 8, 20, 57–59, 81, 83–89,
        91–98, 109, 171–173
    racist, 1
    through regulatory agencies, 62
    significance, 1–4, 3f
    social, 2
    state, 5–11, 13–17, 19–22, 25–29, 49
    tools, 31, 55
        CityHealth framework, 33–37, 36f
        Health Impact in Five Years (HI-5) Model,
            39–45, 41f
        litigation power, 67–78, 68f, 73f
        PHACCS Initiative, 49–53, 50f
        regulatory power, 61–64
Policy Action Institute (2020), 109
policymakers, 36, 102, 104, 150
policymaking, 4, 9, 16
political action committee (PAC), 92
politicians, 91, 116
politics
    consequences of, 116
    engagement in, 172
    power of, 67
    public health and, 57–59, 91
    science and, 9
pollution, 154

population health, 3*f*
    improvement of, 49–53, 50*f*
    prevention efforts, 51
postpartum women, 20
poverty, 2, 40, 154
    federal level, 14–15
    generational, 57, 163
    poor health and, 39, 53
    in Puerto Rico, 13
    rates of, 13, 51
Powell, Colin, 134
predictive analytics, 105
preemption, 74–75
    doctrine, 83
    inequitable, 120
    perils of
        age to purchase tobacco, 87–88
        alcohol sales, 88
        ceiling, 83–84
        CityHealth policies and, 84
        floor, 83–84
        inclusionary zoning, 86
        life expectancy and, 85
        local health policy and, 85, 88–89
        local health risks and, 89
        sick leave, earned, 86–87
        state preemption of local health-promoting
            policies, 85
        when state laws conflict with local policies,
            83–89
    state, 134
    Supremacy Clause and, 83
    vacuum, 84
pregnancy, teenage, 25
pre-Kindergarten programs, 50*f*, 51, 84
    early education investment in
        current context for, 136
        funding for, 135
        policy promotion for high quality and access
            to, 137–140, 138*t*
    Preschool Program Quality Calculator, 139
    quality, 34, 136–137
    teachers, 136
prescription drug coverage, 14
problem-solving skills, 135

Promoting Health and Cost Control in States
    (PHACCS) Initiative, 49–50, 171–172
    economic well-being and, 53
    education and, 51
    goals, 50*f*
    harm reduction and, 51–52
    safe environments and, 52
public
    safety, 36, 39
    transportation, 40, 43
public health
    advocacy, 1, 7–11, 58, 62, 69, 92
    budgets, 91
    challenges, 20, 50
    collaboration across sectors, 21
    creating future change in, 91–98
    crises, 102
    emergency funding for, 13, 15–16, 102
    federal, 171
    funding for, 16, 19, 49
        data modernization initiative, 104–105
    goals, 64
    government, 19
    history of, 8
    infrastructure, 3, 10, 11, 57, 171
    interventions, 101
    legal issues, 67
    litigation, 67–78, 68*f*, 73*f*, 76
    local, 19
    malpractice, 58
    organizations, 4
    outcomes, 25
    PHACCS Initiative goals, 50*f*
    policy, 4, 20
        advancement strategies, 8
        creating future change in, 91–98
        future of, 171–173
        preemption perils, 83–89
        threats to using, 81
    politics and, 57–59, 91
    practitioners, 4, 39–40, 59, 150, 173
        educational initiatives for, 78
    preparedness, 20
    principles, 117
    priorities, 25

role in COVID-19 pandemic, 96
science, 9
state level, 171
  data sources, 20
  educational initiatives, 19, 78
  emergency response, 19
  environmental protections, 19
  health equity and social determinants of
    health, 21–22
  health officials, 19–22
  laws, 83–89
  legislation, 51, 67
  policy, 20–21
  power of, 20
  preemption, 85, 134
  preventive services, 19
  surveillance, 101–102
  underperformance during COVID-19
    pandemic, 91
  workforce, 44, 45, 91
Public Health 3.0, 19–20, 22
Public Health Under Siege, 109
Public Health Workforce Interests and Needs Survey
  (2017), 42
Public Transportation Introduction and Expansion, 40
Public Transportation Public Health Action Guide, 44
Puerto Rico, 13–17

Q

quarantine, government authority to, 67
quasi-defensive litigation, 68f, 72–75, 73f
QuitLine, 73

R

racial bias, 159, 163–164
racial disparities, 37, 159, 164
racial equity training, 161
racial gerrymandering, 77
racial healing, 162–163, 165
racial impact assessments, 163
racial inequities, 21, 159
racial injustice, 93, 167
racial justice, 161, 166, 172–173
racism, 1, 4, 171
  elimination of, 159–167
  institutional, 162

as public health crisis, 160–161, 172
  structural, 154
  systemic, 22, 33, 159, 164
radon, 154
Rapid Rehousing, 50f, 53
regulatory actions, 63, 172
regulatory authority, 64, 75
regulatory capture, 62
regulatory policy, 61–64, 67
religious bigotry, 160
Remley, Karen, 143
rental properties, 131
reproductive health, 71, 107
restaurant
  grading of, 35, 84
  inspections, 64
  smoke-free, 142–144, 144f, 144t
retirement benefits, 87
Robert Wood Johnson Foundation, 40, 96
Roe v. Wade, 71
Rolfe, John, 141
Rosewood Massacre, 166
Rx Racial Healing movement, 160, 163

S

safe school legislation, 116
sanctuary cities, 75
Sandy Hook Elementary, 125–128
San Francisco Department of Health (SFDPH),
  147–148
school
  financing, 117
  nutrition programs, 50f
    free or reduced-price, 51
    healthy snacks for, 51
  readiness, 135
scientific evidence
  policy and, 29
  political influence on, 9
secondhand smoke, 141
segregation, 77, 155, 163
self-censorship, 110
self-regulation, 135
sexism, 160
sexual assault, 150
shelter-in-place orders, 71

shootings
  mass, 125–128
  police-involved, 165
sick leave
  earned, 50f, 53, 83–85
    during COVID-19 pandemic, 35, 87, 147
    medal requirements for, 36f
    preemption and, 86–87
  paid
    first HIA, 148–149
    health inequities without, 148
    HIA findings and, 149–150
    public health role in economic security, 150
    state-mandated, 147
slavery, 162
Slave Trail Commission, 165
smoke-free
  indoor air, 35, 84
  policies, 50f
smoking, 75. See also tobacco
  age, 145
  bans, 71, 83, 141–144, 144f
  cessation, 143
  cigarettes, 63, 69–70, 87, 101, 104, 108
  Family Smoking Prevention and Tobacco Control
    Act of 2009, 74
  rates, 86–87
  regulations, 28
  in restaurants, 142–144, 144f, 144t
  vaping, 19, 25, 104, 108
social determinants of health (SDOH), 2, 3f, 11, 39, 67
  decision-makers for, 40
  definition of, 33
  focus on, 118
  health equity and, 21–22
  into policies, 57
  policy approaches to, 123, 143–145
    elimination of racism, 159–167
    environmental health issues for children,
      153–156
    gun safety in America, 125–128
    paid sick leave, 147–150
    rental inspection policy, 131–134
    tobacco control, 141–142, 144f, 144t
  pre-Kindergarten programs, 50f, 51, 84,
    135–140, 138t

prevention policies that address, 49
public health policy
  future of, 171–173
  public health professionals role in, 42
  that influence community health outcomes, 117
  understanding of, 33–34
social distancing, 163
social justice, 37, 77, 159
social media, 108, 110
social needs, 33–34
social programs, 13
State of Preschool Yearbook, 137–138
streets, complete, 35, 50f, 52, 84
stress, toxic, 22
subject matter experts, 42, 95
substance misuse deaths, 50f
substance use disorder treatment, 69
sugary drinks, warnings on, 73–74
suicide, youth, 128
Supplemental Nutrition Assistance Program
    (SNAP), 9
Supplemental Security Income, 13
Supremacy Clause, 83
syndemic, 2
syringe access programs, 50f, 51
systemic inequities, 33
systemic injustice, 77
systemic racism, 22, 33, 159, 164
systemic separation, 163, 165–166

T

taxes, 9, 40, 43, 166
telehealth, 16
terminology, censored, 107
texting, while driving, 145
tobacco, 1, 8–9, 70, 108, 119
  advertising, 72
  age to purchase, 87–88
  ban, 83
  Campaign for Tobacco-Free Kids, 26
  cessation, 52
  control measures, 27, 67, 141–145, 144f, 144t
  history of, 141
  industry, 76
  laws, 25, 71, 87–88
  as leading cause of preventable death, 52

legal age, 141
litigation, 69
manufacturers, 69
policies, 34
pricing strategies, 50f
regulations, 20
sales, 86
taxes, 141
warnings, 72–73, 73f
Tobacco 21, 25–28, 35–36, 84–85, 87–88
toxic chemicals, 153
trans fat ban, 75
transformation strategy, 113
transformative change, 173
transportation, public, 40, 52
Trump Administration, 63, 156
Trust for America's Health (TFAH), 50, 53
Truth, Racial Healing, and Transformation (TRHT), 161–167
Truth Initiative, 76

U

unconscious bias, 159
unemployment, 2
University of Texas MD Anderson Cancer Center, 26
US Chamber of Commerce, 77

V

vaccination
    administration, 20
    campaigns, 21
    COVID-19, 71
    for infectious diseases, 20
    mandates, 67
    requirements for school, 107

vacuum preemption, 84
vaping, 19, 25. See also smoking; tobacco
    electronic cigarettes and, 63, 70, 87, 101, 104, 108
Virchow, Rudolf, 59
Virginia Department of Health (VDH), 143, 144f
vision testing, 57, 137
voter
    absentee, 58
    disenfranchisement, 77
    registration, 58

W

wage
    minimum, 1, 76, 132, 150
    theft, 150
Wagner, Scott, 132
water
    clean, 1, 70
    Flint water crisis, 57
    Healthy Air and Water Colorado, 96
    lead in, 70
    pollution, 155
What Works for Health, 41
white supremacy, 76
W.K. Kellogg Foundation, 161
World Health Organization, 33
World Trade Organization, 71

X

xenophobia, 160

Z

Zika, 101, 104